15

D1106806

NUCLEAR ASTROPHYSICS

Memoirs of the

AMERICAN PHILOSOPHICAL SOCIETY

Held at Philadelphia
For Promoting Useful Knowledge
Volume 67

® *Copyrighted by the California Institute of Technology, Carnegie Institution of Washington, and General Aniline & Film Corporation.*

The Crab Nebula photographed in color by William Miller of the staff of the Mount Wilson and Palomar Observatories. The nebula consists of the expanding debris of a supernova which was observed as a "guest" star at the same point in the sky by Chinese astronomers in *A.D.* 1054.

NUCLEAR
ASTROPHYSICS

WILLIAM A. FOWLER

Professor of Physics
California Institute of Technology

Jayne Lectures for 1965

AMERICAN PHILOSOPHICAL SOCIETY

INDEPENDENCE SQUARE • PHILADELPHIA

1967

The Jayne Lectures of the American Philosophical Society honor the memory of Henry La Barre Jayne, 1857-1920, a distinguished citizen of Philadelphia and an honored member of the Society. They perpetuate in this respect the aims of the American Society for the Extension of University Teaching, in which Mr. Jayne was deeply interested. When in 1946 this organization was dissolved, having in large measure fulfilled its immediate purposes, its funds were transferred to the American Philosophical Society, which agreed to use them "for the promotion of university teaching, including *inter alia* lectures, publications and research in the fields of science, literature, and the arts."

Accepting this responsibility, the Society initiated in 1961 a series of lectures to be given annually or biennially by outstanding scholars, scientists, and artists, and to be published in book form by the Society. The lectures are presented at various cultural institutions of Philadelphia. Thus far the following, including the series published in the present volume, have been presented:

February 21, 28, March 7, 14, 1961. Per Jacobsson. *The Market Economy in the World of Today.* University Museum, University of Pennsylvania. Memoirs of the American Philosophical Society, Vol. 55 (1961).

March 7, 14, 21, 1962. George Wells Beadle. *Genetics and Modern Biology.* University Museum, University of Pennsylvania. Memoirs of the American Philosophical Society, Vol. 57 (1963).

March 6, 13, 20, 1963. Doris Mary Stenton. *English Justice Between the Norman Conquest and the Great Charter, 1066-1215.* University Museum, University of Pennsylvania. Memoirs of the American Philosophical Society, Vol. 60 (1964).

March 10, 17, 24, 1964, Ellis Kirkham Waterhouse. *Three Decades of British Art: 1740-1770.* Philadelphia Museum of Art. Memoirs of the American Philosophical Society, Vol. 63 (1965).

May 3, 4, 6, 7, 1965. William A. Fowler. *Nuclear Astrophysics.* The Franklin Institute. Memoirs of the American Philosophical Society, Vol. 67 (1967).

Copyright © 1967 by The American Philosophical Society
Library of Congress Catalog Card Number: 67-18204
Reprinted 1968

To

CHARLES CHRISTIAN LAURITSEN

Foreword

For the fifth series of Jayne Lectures, Professor William A. Fowler chose the broadest possible subject short of infinity itself—the evolution of the chemical elements from the hydrogen nucleus of primordial matter to those that now exist on earth, in our sun and myriad other stars, and in the clustered nebulae. His thought reaches, indeed, to celestial objects so distant, so immense, and so recently discovered that their constitution can as yet only be conjectured.

The lecturer's experience and accomplishments are broad enough to qualify him for such an all-embracing survey. Trained as an undergraduate in engineering physics, he took his doctorate in experimental nuclear physics at the California Institute of Technology. As a member of the faculty of that great center of physical science, he had the benefit of association not only with stimulating colleagues, but also with the astronomers and astrophysicists of the Mount Wilson and Palomar Observatories. As a Guggenheim Fellow and Fulbright Lecturer at Cambridge, England, he collaborated with Professor Fred Hoyle and others on theoretical analysis of astrophysics, bringing together the best English and American thought on this vast and complex subject.

To his ability as an investigator and his wide contacts with fellow scientists, Dr. Fowler adds exceptional skill as an expositor of intricate phenomena. At each of his four Jayne Lectures at the Franklin Institute he held a capacity audience, largely composed of advanced students, in concentrated attention followed by vigorous applause. Hearers able to follow readily the lecturer's mathematics and physics were enchanted by his luminous and lively presentation and his forthright statement of his own position on controversial questions. Others, to whom physical and mathematical comprehension does not come easily, found themselves, to their surprise, led on step by step to a delighted appreciation of the logic and the grandeur of cosmic evolution.

GEORGE W. CORNER

Author's Preface

NUCLEAR ASTROPHYSICS is a new and exciting scientific discipline with a remarkable pedigree. It is the offspring of the marriage of nuclear physics and astronomy. In the Jayne Memorial Lectures for 1965, of which this book is an account, I explored some of the many ramifications which arise in that marriage.

In less anthropomorphic terminology, these lectures are concerned with the applications of nuclear physics in astronomy. In moments of overexuberance I have teased my astronomical colleagues with the remark that astronomy is nothing more than applied nuclear physics! This is very far from the whole truth but there is an element of truth in the idea. Nuclear physics is basic to two major problems in astronomy. First of all, the generation of energy in stars, supernovae and other celestial objects arises from the operation of nuclear processes within these objects. Secondly, the generation of nuclear energy requires the transformation of nuclear species into new and more stable forms and thus the synthesis of all the elements and their isotopes heavier than ordinary hydrogen becomes a possibility in the long and varied history of astronomical systems. The generation of nuclear energy and the origin of the elements are recurrent themes in these lectures.

In the W. K. Kellogg Radiation Laboratory and the Alfred P. Sloan Laboratory of Mathematics and Physics at the California Institute of Technology, a long and fruitful investigation of reactions involving the light nuclei has been carried out under the direction of Charles Christian Lauritsen who has only recently "retired" as Emeritus Professor of Physics. In 1938 with the discovery of the carbon-nitrogen cycle independently by Bethe and von Weizsäcker we became aware of the fact that our studies on the interactions of the carbon and nitrogen isotopes with protons, the nuclei of ordinary hydrogen, were relevant to astronomy. During World War II the Kellogg Laboratory was devoted to the development of rocket and atomic ordnance for the United States Navy, but with the conclusion of the war we decided to continue in the field of low energy, light element nuclear physics (contrary to more ambitious aims elsewhere) and to concentrate in good part on the study of those nuclear reactions thought to take place in stars. We were encouraged in this by our colleague, Professor Ira S. Bowen who became at that time the Director of Mount Wilson and new Mount Palomar Observatories. Bowen held a series of informal seminars in his home in which astronomers from the observatories and nuclear physicists from the California Institute discussed problems of mutual interest over beer and pretzels.

Thus nuclear astrophysics became an important part of the research program in our nuclear laboratories. Important contributions have been made over the years by all the faculty staff members, Professors John Bahcall, Charles Barnes, Robert Christy, Ralph Kavanagh, Thomas Lauritsen, Thomas Tombrello and Ward Whaling, as well as by a host of graduate students and visiting research fellows and associates. Notable among the latter is Professor E. E. Salpeter of Cornell who has made so many contributions in the field of nuclear astrophysics.

In 1948 Professor Jesse L. Greenstein came to the California Institute to lead the work in astronomy and his interest in the abundances of the elements in stars has stimulated much of our work. In 1954-1955 I spent a sabbatical year as a Fulbright lecturer and Guggenheim fellow in the Cavendish Laboratory at the University of Cambridge. There began what has been for me an inspiring and fruitful collaboration with Fred Hoyle, the Plumian Professor at Cambridge, and Geoffrey and Margaret Burbidge, now professors at the University of California, San Diego (La Jolla). Even before 1954, Fred Hoyle had triggered our long and extensive investigations of the production of carbon from helium by predicting the existence of a new excited state of the nucleus C^{12} on the basis of his analysis of the two stage process involving the amalgamation of three helium nuclei originally suggested by Salpeter. I well remember our skepticism until Professor Whaling and his collaborators discovered this exciting, excited state.

The work continues in our laboratories and in many others. Our studies have been supported in part, continuously since 1946, by the Office of Naval Research of the United States Navy, for a short period by the National Aeronautics and Space Administration, and for the last few years also by the National Science Foundation. The Jayne Memorial Lectures for 1965 are, in one sense, a report to the public of our stewardship in the expenditure of public funds. In another sense, they constitute an account for the enlightened layman and student of the current state of affairs in nuclear astrophysics. The author is grateful to the American Philosophical Society and the Franklin Institute of Philadelphia for the opportunity to report and account. He is also indebted to the California Institute of Technology for sabbatical leave and to the Massachusetts Institute of Technology for hospitality during the period in which the final manuscript for this monograph was produced.

WILLIAM A. FOWLER

Pasadena, June, 1966

Contents

Illustrations

I. The Origin of the Elements

WHEN WE LOOK ABOUT US at the objects of the physical world we observe matter in forms of almost infinite variety and complexity. Even the most commonplace objects in our immediate surroundings—this table, this blackboard, even this piece of chalk—are clearly not simple in structure or composition. For the scientist, with methods of observation which transcend the powers of the five human senses, the variety and complexity is even more apparent and overwhelming. Whether he looks up to the stars or down to the depths of the earth, he sees a chemistry of creation wondrous in its countless forms and variations.

We know that even early man tried to reach some understanding of the material world about him by thinking of these complicated forms as being made up of the more common and thus the more simply comprehensible substances of which he was aware. The men of ancient Greece thought that the elementary forms of matter and energy—out of which all other forms could be produced—were air, earth, fire, and water. Later they became even more sophisticated and postulated that matter consists of very small, indivisible, indestructible and uncreatable atoms. Medieval men returned to the commonplace substances—their elements were water, oil, earth, sulfur, salt, and air.

During the eighteenth and nineteenth centuries all matter was found to be composed of atoms of what were termed the chemical elements—hydrogen, helium, oxygen, sodium, iron, gold, lead, uranium, to name a few. Gases, liquids and solids, crystals and molecules could all be reduced in turn to the atoms of the elements of the periodic table. These elements were found to be immutable when subjected to the chemical and physical processes known at that time. They were the indestructible building blocks from which the universe was built.

The twentieth century has changed all this. The nuclear physicist has found that the elements are not immutable. The ancient alchemist's dream has come true in the modern nuclear laboratory. Elements can be transmuted one to the other. These transmutations were first unleashed in the atomic bomb and later in the hydrogen bomb. Controlled transmutations in nuclear-fission reactors supply power for cities and submarines. It is known that these processes take place in stars and serve as the source of energy for the light which they radiate and we will find an intimate connection between this energy generation and the origin of the elements—the problem with which we are concerned.

ATOMS AND ISOTOPES

In his experiments, the nuclear physicist discovered the nature of atomic structure: each atom consists of a very small central *nucleus* surrounded by satellite *electrons*. The mass of the atom is concentrated almost entirely in the nucleus. The electrons move in a cloudlike region which is much larger than the nucleus. If we can imagine an atom magnified to the dimensions of a football stadium, the central nucleus would be the size of a garden pea and the electron cloud would take up the rest of the space.

In ordinary matter, nuclei have a positive electric charge while electrons have a negative charge. The neutral atom has no over-all charge because the number of negative electrons surrounding the nucleus is just enough to balance the positive nuclear charge. The number and distribution of electrons determine almost entirely the commonplace chemical, physical, and electrical properties of the atom. Thus these properties depend indirectly on the charge of the nucleus. The atoms of one element are distinguished from those of another by the nuclear charge and the corresponding number of electrons. For example, the nuclei of hydrogen have a single positive charge. In the hydrogen atom this is balanced by one negatively charged electron. The nucleus of uranium has 92 times the charge of hydrogen nuclei, and this charge is balanced in the uranium atom by 92 electrons.

At first sight it would seem we have made things much more complicated than the simple ideas of the ancient Greeks and the medievalists. For one thing, there are now known to be 104 elements or atomic species—from hydrogen, the lightest, to khurchatovium, named for I. V. Khurchatov, the great Russian nuclear physicist, which has nuclei with 104 times the charge of hydrogen nuclei. In addition to the great number of elements there is another point of complexity. Although the nuclei of a given element all have the same electrical charge, they do not all have the same mass. These differing forms are called *isotopes* and all the isotopes of a given element have the same chemical properties in spite of their differing mass.

TABLE 1

ELEMENTS		ISOTOPES	
Stable	81	Stable	280
Technetium (Stars)	1	Nat. Radioactivity	67
		Art. Radioactivity	1164
Promethium	1		
Thru Bismuth	83	TOTAL	1511
		March, 1965	
Nat. Radioactivity	9		
Thru Uranium	92		
Art. Radioactivity	12		
Thru Element 104	104		
Neutron	1		
TOTAL	105		

Nuclei = Neutrons + Protons

Example: $C^{12} = 6N + 6P$

No Stable Mass 5 or Mass 8

The great number of the known elements and their isotopes is presented in table 1. Ninety elements are found terrestrially and one more, technetium, has been observed spectroscopically in stars; promethium and those with nuclear charge greater than 92 have not been found in nature. There are 81 stable elements in the range from hydrogen to element 83, bismuth,

the last element in the periodic table, which has a stable
isotope. Nine elements from polonium (84) to uranium (92)
are found in natural radioactivity because of the long lifetimes
of the parents of the three radioactive series. These parents
are the nuclei $_{90}Th^{232}$, $_{92}U^{235}$ and $_{92}U^{238}$ where Th designates
the element thorium, U designates the element uranium, the
numerical subscript designates the atomic (element) number,
and the numerical superscript the mass in good approximation
relative to that of hydrogen, the lightest and first element.
(The atomic number is frequently omitted, viz: Th^{232}, U^{235},
U^{238} and in Europe the atomic mass superscript is frequently
placed to the left, viz.: ^{232}Th, ^{235}U, ^{238}U.) These nuclei are
unstable to the emission of alpha-particles or helium nuclei[1] but
the half-lives[2] are 14, 0.7 and 4.5 billion years respectively.
Thus these nuclei and their daughter products exist terrestrially
because their lifetimes are comparable to the age of the earth
and the solar system which geologists estimate to be around
4.5 billion years.

   Some 280 stable and 67 naturally radioactive isotopes occur
on the earth, making a total of 347. In addition, the neutron
(n), technetium (Tc), promethium (Pm) and the transuranic
elements up to number 104 have been produced artificially,
that is by the bombardment of lighter nuclear species with
another in man-made accelerators or reactors. Technetium and
promethium are unique among the elements below bismuth
in that they have no stable isotopes. The longest-lived radioactive forms are $_{43}Tc^{97}$ with a half-life of 2.6 million years and

---

[1] I will commonly designate these nuclei by the symbol $_2He^4$ or just He^4
although they are frequently designated by the Greek letter α. They were
called alpha-particles by Lord Rutherford since they were the *first* particles
identified in natural radioactive decay. Subsequently, beta-particles were
identified as negative electrons and gamma-rays as high energy light quanta.

[2] The half-life of a radioactive nucleus is the time in which one-half of
any given initial number of these nuclei decay to the daughter products. In
the first half-life, one-half decay; in the second half-life, one-half of the
remainder or one-quarter of the original number decay; in the third half-life,
one-half of the remainder or one-eighth of the original number decay, and
so on. This can be stated in another way. If we count the number remaining
after a succession of time intervals equal to the half-life, we will find $\frac{1}{2}$, $\frac{1}{4}$,
$\frac{1}{8}$, $\frac{1}{16}$, $\frac{1}{32}$ . . . of the original number.

$_{61}Pm^{145}$ with a half-life of only 18 years. Even if the earth originally contained Tc and Pm, these elements have long since decayed to undetectable amounts.

The number of radioactive isotopes artificially produced was 1,164 as of March, 1965, and this number is gradually increasing, about 20 new forms being discovered each year. In regard to atomic mass numbers, all masses from 1 to 238 are found terrestrially with the important exceptions of mass 5 and mass 8. When nuclei with these mass numbers are produced in the laboratory they are found to have exceedingly short lifetimes, 10^{-21} second for $_2He^5$ and $_3Li^5$ and 10^{-16} second for $_4Be^8$. The symbols designate helium, lithium, and beryllium respectively. Laboratory techniques have extended the radioactive mass numbers beyond 238 to approximately 260. The total number of nuclear species was 1,511 in March of 1965, about one-quarter of this number being known to occur in nature and three-quarters having been produced artificially. In the origin of the elements and their isotopes we shall find that the radioactive forms often play an even more important role than the stable forms to which they decay in nature. It is frequently the radioactive forms which are first produced in the element-building processes.

NUCLEI AND NUCLEONS

But is 1,511 the number of the fundamental units of matter? Fortunately, the answer is no! In 1932 the riddle of this apparent complexity was solved; all nuclei were shown to consist of two still more fundamental building blocks, the *proton* (*p*) and the *neutron,* collectively called *nucleons.* The proton is the central nucleus of the ordinary hydrogen atom (H^1).[3] The proton has a single positive charge, equal in

---

[3] The reader will find that I often use H^1, the atomic symbol, for the proton in nuclear reactions. This has come about because in most cases the nuclear and atomic symbols are the same. Thus Li^7 designates either the mass-seven nucleus of lithium or the atom which it forms with three extra nuclear electrons. In the same way H^1 is used for the proton. Similarly H^2 or D^2 or just D are used for the atom of heavy hydrogen, deuterium, or for its nucleus, the deuteron. To further confuse the issue the deuteron (but not deuterium) is frequently designated by *d*.

magnitude but opposite in sign to that of the negative electron, and slightly more than one unit of mass in the measuring system used by the nuclear physicist. The neutron also has slightly more than one unit of mass, but has zero electric charge; it is electrically neutral—thus the word *neutron*. In table 1, I include the neutron in the grand total given as 105. This is to say that at the present time there are 105 values for the electrical charge of the known nuclei. The neutron can not form an *atom* so there are only 104 elements. Purists say 104.

Neutrons in a vacuum or free state transform to positive protons and negative electrons—always in combination, to preserve the over-all charge at zero. Inside stable nuclei, neutrons can retain their own identity and are just as good building blocks as the protons. In some radioactive nuclei neutrons are unstable while in others it is the protons which are unstable. In the former case the neutron transforms to a proton inside the nucleus and a negative electron is emitted. In the latter case the proton transforms to a neutron and a positive electron or positron is emitted. After emission from a radioactive nucleus the positron eventually collides with an electron in the surrounding medium with the result that both are annihilated with the emission of energetic radiation. Because positrons annihilate electrons they are often called *anti-electrons*. I will have more to say about annihilation in what follows. Pairs of positrons and electrons can also be produced in the laboratory or in nature by the interaction of high energy radiation with nuclei. We can complete this description of the type of radioactivity under discussion, which is called *beta-decay,* by noting that particles called *neutrinos* are always emitted with the positrons and that particles called *antineutrinos* are always emitted with the electrons. These particles are the main characters in our second lecture and will be described in some detail therein. In another type of beta-decay activity a proton in an unstable nucleus captures one of the atomic electrons surrounding the nucleus and is transformed in this way into a neutron. In the transformation a neutrino is emitted. At the high temperatures which occur in stars toward the end of their existence, positron-electron pairs are created in great abundance. Under these circumstances positron-capture with antineutrino emission can also occur. In addition, pair annihilation can result in the production of a neutrino and an antineutrino.

Let us return to the problem of the composition of nuclei. Each of the 1,511 nuclear species is characterized by a definite number of protons and a definite number of neutrons. Since the neutron has zero charge, the charge of a nucleus, its atomic number, is given by the number of protons it contains. Since the neutron and proton have approximately the same mass, the mass of a nucleus is given by the sum of the numbers of protons and neutrons it contains. For example, there are three variants, or isotopes, of uranium found in nature. The lightest is $_{92}U^{234}$ and the other two are $_{92}U^{235}$ and $_{92}U^{238}$ which have been mentioned previously. All of these nuclei contain 92 protons so the number of neutrons which they contain must be 142, 143, and 146 respectively.

Thus we see that atoms with the same number of protons but differing numbers of neutrons in their nuclei are isotopes of the same element. In ordinary physical and chemical processes isotopes behave alike. In nuclear processes, however, isotopes behave quite differently because of the differing numbers of neutrons. In other words, these differences in isotopes are not important under ordinary circumstances; only in the nuclear laboratory or reactor or at the high temperature and density in the center of stars do the isotopes of an element play their individual nuclear roles.

Because of their chemical identity the relative amounts of the isotopes of one element remain unchanged in most geological processes. The ten isotopes of the element tin, for example, have come down to us unchanged in their relative numbers since they were produced in cosmic events. They tell us of the nuclear history of the universe, and in these lectures it will be seen that we have learned to look upon the isotopes of the elements as truly eternal clues. Gold, in spite of its economic charm for human beings, is useless in this regard—it has only one stable isotope: $_{79}Au^{197}$.

The proof of nuclear structure comes from experiments in

nuclear laboratories. These experiments have shown that all nuclei can be dissociated into neutrons and protons and all can be fused or put together again from these same nucleons. This must not be taken too literally. Protons and neutrons almost certainly do not retain their exact identity once inside nuclei. Their internal structure may be greatly disturbed. Great progress has been made in high energy nuclear physics in understanding the internal structure of the nucleons, but the story is by no means complete. However, in most acts of the drama of creation the nucleons may be considered immutable.

This immutability of nucleons is not inviolate. When nuclear collisions occur at high velocity and great energy in the nuclear laboratory, particles called *antiprotons* can be created in pairs with protons. Antiprotons have exactly the same mass as protons but have a negative charge equal to that of the electron and thus equal in magnitude but opposite in sign to that of the proton. An antiproton escapes with considerable velocity from the proton with which it is born. In ordinary matter it eventually meets another proton which it annihilates along with itself in a great burst of energy. Similarly, *antineutrons* which annihilate neutrons can be produced in pairs with neutrons. A discussion of the difference between neutrons and antineutrons, both of which are electrically neutral, will come in the next chapter. The nomenclature for these new particles is quite literal and graphic—*antinucleons* annihilate nucleons, *antimatter* annihilates matter!

Thus, protons and neutrons can be created and destroyed but always in processes involving antiprotons and antineutrons. The creation requires extremely high energies of interaction. The destruction requires antimatter. What is the situation in our surroundings where the energies of interaction are relatively low and where antiparticles are certainly very rare? I have pointed out previously that free neutrons and some neutrons in radioactive nuclei can transform to protons with the emission of electrons and antineutrinos. I have also pointed out that protons in certain other radioactive nuclei can transform to neutrons with the emission of positrons and neutrons.

However, in low energy interactions, in a world of our kind of matter, protons and neutrons, collectively as nucleons, are stable and immutable. In other words, the total number of protons and neutrons remains constant even though transformations between them take place. This is in spite of the fact that no previously known laws prevent them from transforming entirely to electrons and other lighter particles with the disappearance of mass and the release of large amounts of energy. For this reason we have to accept another law of nature: Nucleons at low energy and well separated from antinucleons are immutable. If this law did not hold, then the universe as we know it would not exist.

With this picture of the structure of the nuclei of the elements in mind, it is natural to attempt to explain their origin by a *nucleosynthesis* starting with the fundamental building blocks, the protons and neutrons. Here I will not attempt to account for the origin or *nucleogenesis* of the protons and neutrons. Some cosmologists believe that nucleons have always existed and that the question of their origin is not a proper scientific problem. I must say that I have little sympathy with this point of view. Other cosmologists believe in a steady-state cosmology in which nucleons are constantly being created. The creation of the nucleons makes up for the expansion of the universe in maintaining the mean density of matter at a steady-state value. Still other cosmologists think that the nucleons were created many billions of years ago in a primordial event.

Both the latter points of view have the common difficulty that we only know of processes in which nucleons are created in pairs with antinucleons—and antinucleons annihilate nucleons. We live in a world of nucleons. How did our nucleons escape completely from the set of annihilating antinucleons with which they were born? Do there exist other astronomical systems which consist of *antiatoms* made up of *antinuclei* surrounded by antielectrons, with the antinuclei made up in turn of antiprotons and antineutrons? The Swedish cosmologists Otto Klein and Hannes Alfvén say yes, and have proposed a universe originally composed of equal amounts of matter and antimatter in which segregation processes have subsequently taken place. Observationally, no one really knows.

It is known that the solar system and probably the galaxy in which it is located, the Milky Way, consist of what we call matter and not antimatter. Thus the basic problem as far as we are concerned reduces to this question: Given protons and neutrons as the building blocks, how and when were they put together in various combinations to form the elements and all of their isotopes? How did the complexity come to be, starting with universal simplicity?

It will be apparent that our primary concern is to be the synthesis of nuclei from protons and neutrons. In order to build atoms and molecules it is also necessary to have electrons. Although the atomic and molecular processes which have happened subsequent to nucleosynthesis are fascinating and in many ways still very puzzling, nevertheless I will not dwell upon them in detail in these lectures. It will suffice to assume that there are enough electrons to balance the charge on the protons so that matter in the bulk remains electrically neutral. There are nuclear processes in which electrons, as well as positrons, neutrinos, and antineutrinos play a role and these, of course, will be of great interest to us. All of this can be said in another way—our concern is primarily with the nuclear physics of element building and only peripherally with the chemistry, fascinating as the latter may be.

THE ABUNDANCE DISTRIBUTION OF THE ELEMENTS

Before turning to mechanisms of nucleosynthesis let me briefly discuss some quantitative information on the relative abundance of the elements by mass as presented in table 2. The numbers in table 2 pertain primarily to the solar system. The observational evidence has been obtained by chemical and physical measurements on meteorites and the earth's crust and by deductions from the spectrum of light from the sun and certain other stars which are very similar in composition to the sun. Each element produces characteristic absorption and emission lines in stellar spectra and thus the spectra can be

analyzed to indicate the element abundance in the light-
emitting region of a star. The data in table 2 were at one
time taken to represent a "universal" or "cosmic" abundance
distribution. It is now known that many stars exhibit light
spectra which indicate an element composition quite different
from that observed in the sun. I will return to this point later
in the lecture. Whether or not table 2 represents a truly
universal abundance distribution is not of too great relevance.
It is the distribution for the great bulk of the matter on which
we have been able to make observations. It holds for "our"
matter and we can seek the history of this particular matter.
We can also ask, as our knowledge increases, for the history
of the peculiar and abnormal abundances (peculiar and abnormal to us!) observed in some stars. In time, we may obtain
more information of the abundances in other parts of our
Galaxy and in other galaxies, sufficient to reveal the detailed
history of nucleosynthesis throughout the universe.

TABLE 2

RELATIVE ABUNDANCE OF THE ELEMENTS BY MASS

Elements	Fractional Abundance by Mass
Hydrogen: H^1; D^2	0.71; 10^{-4}
Helium: He^4; He^3	0.27; 6×10^{-5}
Li, Be, B	10^{-8}
C, N, O, Ne	1.8×10^{-2}
Silicon Group: Na to Ti	2×10^{-3}
Iron Group: $50 \leqslant A \leqslant 62$	2×10^{-4}
Middleweight Group: $63 \leqslant A \leqslant 100$	10^{-6}
Heavyweight Group: $A > 100$	10^{-7}

Table 2 reveals that the gases hydrogen and helium make up
approximately 98 per cent of the bulk of the solar system.
This is obviously not the case for the earth or the meteorites
or most of the other planets. The answer to this puzzle is that
the earth and the other planets did not have gravitational
fields large enough to retain hydrogen and helium against
thermal escape in their original formation. The planet Jupiter

is an exception in this regard. Presumably, the parent body
or bodies of the meteorites were also not large enough. On
the other hand, both solar spectra and the theory of solar
structure indicate that the sun is mostly hydrogen. Since it
was large enough to retain primordial hydrogen, the sun is
taken as a better sample in this regard than other components
of the solar system. The case of helium is even more indirect.
It is difficult to detect helium spectroscopically in the sun,
and the value given in table 2 is actually taken from spectra
of nearby stars with higher surface temperatures in which
helium spectral lines can be excited. The sun is assumed
to have the same He/H ratio as these hotter stars, an assumption which is open to some question, since it is known that
these stars have formed more recently than the sun. However,
calculations on the structure of the sun depend on the He/H
ratio, and the results are not inconsistent with the value
$0.27 \div 0.71 = 0.38$ by mass given in table 2. This value is
thus taken to hold for the primordial ratio in the material
from which the sun formed. The outer parts of the sun should
still exhibit this ratio on the reasonable assumption that little
mixing has occurred with the interior. Hydrogen has been
converted into helium in the interior in the process which
serves as the source of energy in the sun. In the center of
the sun He/H now equals ~ 1 by mass.

The elements carbon (C), nitrogen (N), oxygen (O), and
neon (Ne) make up almost all of the 2 per cent of the solar
system which is not hydrogen or helium. The so-called light
elements, lithium, beryllium, and boron (B) and the very
heavy elements are very rare indeed. The elements from
sodium (Na) to scandium (Sc) plus those in the iron group,
titanium (Ti) through nickel (Ni), add up to only 0.2 per
cent or one-tenth of C, N, O, and Ne. On the assumption that
light hydrogen was the primordial material, we thus can argue
that only 26 per cent has been converted to mass 4 and only
2 per cent to all the heavier masses taken together. *Thus any
mechanism of element formation by build-up need not be
overworked.* On the other hand, element formation from
large composite nuclear structures requires almost complete

fragmentation and thus, to some at least, would seem less reasonable and less probable. In any case I will not discuss theories of nucleosynthesis along these lines.

NUCLEOSYNTHESIS IN A SINGLE PRIMORDIAL EVENT

Just as there are two antithetic theories of the origin of the nucleons, the continuous creation and the single creation, so there are two divergent points of view concerning the synthesis of the elements beyond hydrogen. In one point of view, George Gamow and his collaborators, Robert Alpher and Robert Herman, have appealed to the astronomical evidence for the expanding universe. This evidence shows that the light from other galaxies is shifted in color to the red. A simple and intuitively satisfying interpretation of these observations is that these shifts indicate that the distant galaxies are receding from us. The light we receive from them is reddened and the radio waves are lengthened just as the sound from the whistle of a receding train is shifted toward the bass. The observations also show that the more distant a galaxy the greater its red shift and thus, on this point of view, the greater its velocity of recession. In my third lecture I will discuss the difficulties which arise when ordinary concepts such as distance and velocity are used in interpreting observations on objects in the depths of space. For the moment I will adopt the point of view that the red shift is due to recessional velocity. This point of view suggests a primordial "big bang," in which all the matter of our universe was ejected with high velocity from a common region; the galaxies whose matter received the greatest velocities relative to that of our own are now the most distant from us. The distances to the galaxies divided by the velocities as deduced from the red shifts fix the time of the creation. This turns out to be seven to fifteen billion years ago.

Holding to the explosive evolutionary cosmology and the expanding universe, Gamow suggested that in the early stages of the expansion the average density and temperature of radiation and matter were very great indeed compared to present-day values, and that under these circumstances neutrons rather than protons and electrons were the major constituents of matter. And so, *in the beginning,* Gamow postulates a huge "neutron ball" bathed in radiation that promptly began to expand because of its great internal energy. This "ylem" was the primordial material at the start of the expansion of the universe which we now observe billions of years after the original "big bang."

The nuclear processes which took place during the early stages of the expanding universe can be studied in the nuclear laboratory. I have mentioned that neutrons in vacuum transform to protons, electrons, and antineutrinos. This transformation takes time and, in the case of the neutron, the half-life is found to be twelve minutes. Thus, as the primeval expansion took place, neutrons gradually changed into protons, electrons, and antineutrinos. For the moment let us forget about the electrons and antineutrinos, recalling only that the electrons serve to maintain the electrical neutrality of the ylem even when the neutrons decay.

Again laboratory observations tell us something relevant. When neutrons are produced in hydrogen gas, rather than in a vacuum, they fuse together very rapidly with the protons in the hydrogen atoms: the protons are said to capture the neutrons. Gamow thought of this happening during the primeval expansion. One of the free neutrons transforms. The proton from this transformation captures one of the remaining free neutrons. The result is the formation of the deuteron, the nucleus of an isotope of hydrogen called "heavy" hydrogen. The deuteron has a mass twice that of the proton or neutron. The first of the nuclear species beyond ordinary hydrogen has been produced.

The deuteron can in turn capture another free neutron to form the triton, a still heavier form of hydrogen with a mass of three units, but still with the single positive electrical charge of the original proton. At this stage, experiments show that one or the other of the two captured neutrons in the triton emits an electron and becomes a proton, leaving a nucleus with two protons—and the remaining neutron—and therefore a positive charge of two units and a mass of three units. This makes the resultant atom an isotope of helium, whose nuclei are doubly charged. A new element has been formed. The common form of helium has a mass of four units, and this comes into being when the helium with three mass units captures a neutron to keep the chain of events going.

Thus, according to this theory, by a succession of neutron captures, interspersed from time to time by electron emission to form protons in the synthesized nuclei, all of the elements were built in a matter of a few minutes during the earliest epoch of the expanding universe.

This picture of the creation and the element-building, followed rapidly by the formation of galaxies, stars, and planets, seemed to be demanded by the astronomical evidence when it was proposed some years ago. At that time the age of the universe was thought to be the same as that of the solar system, namely 4.5 billion years. This suggested that the elements, the galaxies, the stars and the planets had been created in a relatively short time. Recent research has set the age of the universe as at least 7 billion years—while the solar-system age remains at 4.5 billion years—so a somewhat less hectic early history is now possible, even in this evolutionary picture of cosmology.

There are widely recognized difficulties in the foregoing element-synthesis chain. One difficulty is the lifetime of the triton, twelve years; in the short interval of the "big bang" (approximately one hour) few of the tritons decay to He^3 which captures a neutron to produce He^4. The most striking difficulty arises from the fact that among all the nuclear species found in nature, none has a mass of five or a mass of eight units as previously noted. When produced in the laboratory, nuclei with these masses break up again very rapidly. Thus the chain of neutron-capture events—one unit of mass at a time—has two broken links. We are forced to conclude that only the lightest elements could have been produced in the primeval explosion.

Valiant efforts were made by Anthony Turkevich and the late Enrico Fermi to circumvent these difficulties. The problem has been reopened recently by groups at California Institute of Technology and at Princeton. Reactions between the protons and deuterons and other charged particles have been taken into account. The primordial proton-neutron ratio has been given the thermodynamically correct value rather than the very low value assumed by Gamow. The electron-positron pairs and neutrino-antineutrino pairs produced by the intense radiation field have been included. Photodisintegrations induced by the radiation field have been taken into account. These conclusions have confirmed the conviction that the big bang nucleosynthesis practically terminates at He^4 and that the end result is hydrogen (H^1) and helium (He^4) with the relative proportions of these two elements depending critically on the value assumed for the primordial density. Small amounts of D^2, He^3, Li^7 and B^{11} are also produced. If the assumed density is too low, most of the neutrons will decay into protons and electrons before being captured by other particles and the resultant material will be almost exclusively hydrogen. If, on the contrary, the density is taken too high, everything would be built into helium and no hydrogen will be left.

The Japanese investigators, Hayashi and Nishida, postulated a "matter" universe of very much greater material density than that assumed by Gamow and even succeeded in building as far as neon, the tenth element, but no further. Since their calculations of element abundances did not yield close correspondence with observation and since the elements heavier than neon were not produced at all, their point of view has not been generally accepted.

One of the major conclusions to be drawn from Gamow's nucleosynthesis in a single primordial event is that the relative abundances of the elements should be the same in all astronomical systems. From spectroscopic observations with telescopes this is known not to be true even for the stars in the Milky Way. There is abundant evidence that the abundance distributions in many stars are quite different from the distribution in the solar system. This is inexplicable on the basis of a single synthesizing event which produced a "universal" distribution. I will return to this point in more detail later in this and the subsequent lectures.

A basic difficulty with primeval synthesis involving charged-particle reactions during early stages of the universal expansion is just the expansion itself. As a result of the expansion, the temperature and density of matter are decreasing with time. Element synthesis involves the production of nuclear forms with increasing charge and increasing electric barriers to other charged particles. All nuclei are positively charged and like charges repel each other. Nuclear physics would seem to require some charged particle interactions in any point of view of element synthesis. To overcome the increasing barriers, nuclear encounters of greater energy and greater frequency are required. Thus, the temperature and density should in general increase with time rather than decrease, as they do in the expanding universe. I shall now turn to a point of view in which this fundamental condition is met.

Nucleosynthesis in Stars

On this point of view, nucleosynthesis has taken place and is still taking place in stars. Its most ardent champion over the years has been Fred Hoyle, the Plumian Professor at Cambridge University, England. Geoffrey and Margaret Burbidge of the University of California at San Diego have collaborated with Hoyle and me for more than a decade in research studies in this field. Many scientists have made significant contributions ever since the idea of nuclear processes operating in stars was advanced by Eddington (and others) almost fifty years ago. In the past twenty years, laboratory and field experiments have demonstrated empirically all the general types of nuclear reactions theoretically necessary to synthesize the stable elements and their isotopes in stars. If stellar explosions are included, then the synthesis of the progenitors of the naturally radioactive nuclei can also be understood. In addition, recent astronomical observations on abundance anomalies in peculiar stars; on the connections among stellar age, composition, evolution, and population type; and on the exchange of matter between stars and the interstellar medium have confirmed and extended the astrophysical basis for this point of view.

The idea of nucleosynthesis in stars is based on the fact that the source of energy in stars is reactions among nuclei and that exoergic nuclear reactions which release energy must

involve transmutations of nuclei of low stability into nuclei
of great stability. Fusion from hydrogen up to the most stable
nuclei in the iron group through charged-particle reactions and
neutron capture thereafter will be expected to play an important part. Stars are not just points of light in the sky. They
are enormous concentrations of glowing matter shining on
nuclear energy like the sun but so far distant that even through
the largest telescopes they are indistinguishable from point
objects.

In connection with this discussion I must emphasize the more
or less obvious fact that what the astronomer sees is the surface
of the sun or other stars. Thus the spectra are characteristic
of the composition of the surface and not of the interior. It
seems to be the case that in the majority of stars there has
been no mixing between surface and interior over the lifetime
of the star. Thus the spectra give no direct indication of the
nuclear processes which occur principally in the central regions
of the star. It can be concluded that the spectroscopic evidence
indicates the composition of the material from which the star
originally formed. This conclusion is of the greatest importance in the interpretation and explanation of the composition
of stars. There are, of course, exceptions. Certain stars give
evidence of deep mixing and thus their surface material is
contaminated with the products of the nuclear process taking
place in their interiors. These stars yield information on the
detailed nature of certain nuclear processes and as exceptions
to the general rule are especially important in elucidating the
mechanisms of nucleosynthesis in stars.

What was the primordial material from which our Galaxy,
the Milky Way, was formed? Clearly, for an answer, it is
necessary for the astronomer to examine the spectra of the
oldest stars now observable, that is, of those stars formed
early in the history of the Galaxy. The evidence is fairly
definite on one point and quite contradictory and indefinite
on another. Observations on the oldest stars definitely indicate
that the abundances of the elements heavier than helium are
as low as 0.1 to 1 per cent of the corresponding abundance in
the solar system: It will be recalled that this solar system

value was only 2 per cent of the total so in these stars the total abundance beyond helium is very low indeed and they must consist almost entirely of hydrogen and perhaps some helium.

It is in regard to the helium to hydrogen ratio that considerable uncertainty exists. Helium is difficult to detect spectroscopically and this may account for the fact that it has not been observed in some stars, both old and young. It has been detected in other stars and whenever an abundance value can be determined it seems to be about the same as that for the sun. In certain old stars no helium can be detected in the surface layers. Whether this means that the original matter of these stars contained no helium is a matter of considerable controversy.

Of course the simplest assumption to make is that the primordial material of the Galaxy was hydrogen. This hydrogen could have originated as the material "created" to sustain the universe in the steady-state cosmology. It could also have originated in a primeval explosive phase of the universe in which nucleosynthesis beyond hydrogen may or may not have taken place. Again the simplest assumption is that synthesis of the elements heavier than hydrogen did not take place at that time; the "creation" of a neutron "ball" was followed during expansion only by neutron decay to protons and electrons and the subsequent formation of neutral hydrogen atoms. However, this simple assumption may not be correct and, as we have seen, there may have been some helium, but little or no heavier elements, produced in the big bang. The arguments go round and round. Some scientists argue that the helium abundance is universal and that this proves that a single synthesizing event which went as far as helium did occur. Others argue that the formation and explosion of very massive stars occurred early in the history of our Galaxy and produced almost all of the helium now observed. Still others question the uniformity and accept the low values for helium observed in a few old stars. They agree that helium production must have been more rapid during the early history of the Galaxy but consider this a normal aspect of nucleosynthesis in stars.

The question of the primordial helium abundance is one of the most interesting of the current problems in astrophysical research. On the other hand, there can be no doubt that the primordial abundance of the elements beyond helium was very small indeed. The theme of these lectures will be that nucleosynthesis in stars was responsible for the production of the heavy elements beyond helium in the sun and other stars of the Galaxy and that it may even have been responsible for the helium production probably in early massive stars. At this stage in the discussion there is one point which must be clearly appreciated. *Stellar nucleosynthesis can occur within the framework of any cosmology, and in particular in either the explosive-evolutionary or the steady-state cosmologies.* It is true that the steady-state cosmology, with no primordial explosive event, demands stellar nucleosynthesis and it was the adherents of this cosmology who were the early supporters of this mode of element synthesis. However, stellar nucleosynthesis fits into the explosive-evolutionary cosmology if it is granted that the primordial explosion resulted in the production of hydrogen, perhaps some helium, but very little if any heavier elements. Nuclear astrophysics can certainly contribute to the resolution of the cosmological problem but, in addition, other lines of research must be pursued to establish that cosmology which best describes the observable universe.

Permit me, in what follows, one idiosyncrasy. I like beginnings and origins to be as simple as possible. In addition, I wish to discuss with you the full gamut of possibilities inherent in stellar nucleosynthesis. Thus I shall take it that the primordial material of the Galaxy was pure hydrogen and shall not again remind you of the many qualifications in regard to helium, except when it is critical to the argument at hand.

THE ASTRONOMICAL SETTING

It is now appropriate for us to consider the astronomical setting for nucleosynthesis in stars. Astronomers speak of the system of stars of which the sun is a part as the Galaxy, with a capital G, no less. We see part of it as the Milky Way. The Galaxy is one of seventeen galaxies making up the so-called

FIG. 1. The Virgo Cluster, a group of associated galaxies in the constellation Virgo taken with the U. S. Naval Observatory 61-inch Astrometric Reflector, Flagstaff, Arizona. (*Official U. S. Navy Photograph. Courtesy of* Dr. Kaj Strand.)

local cluster of galaxies. The nearest group of galaxies to the local group is 40 million light years[4] away. It is called the Virgo Cluster and is illustrated in figure 1. There are many such clusters, some containing a great number of galaxies as members and the study of these clusters has been one of the most intriguing and rewarding in astronomy. They indicate structure in the Universe on the enormous scale of many millions of light years.

Our nearest neighbor galaxy in our own cluster is the Andromeda Nebula illustrated in figure 2. It is 2 million light years away. The Galaxy is a flattened, spiral system somewhat similar to the Andromeda Nebula, its "twin." If

---

[4] The light year is the distance traveled by light in one year. Since the speed of light is 3×10^{10} or thirty billion centimeters per second, and since the year contains approximately 3×10^7 or thirty million seconds, the light year is approximately equal to 10^{18} or one billion billion centimeters.

FIG. 2. The Andromeda Nebula, the great spiral galaxy in *Andromeda*, which is the "twin" of the Galaxy in which the solar system is located. (*Mount Wilson and Palomar Observatories.*)

the sun were located in Andromeda, it would be in one of the spiral arms about two-thirds of the way out or 30,000 light years distant from the bright central core or nucleus of the galaxy. It is the spiral arm of the Galaxy in which we are embedded which we see as the Milky Way. The greater part of the Galaxy is hidden from visible observation by great clouds of obscuring gas and dust. Radio waves can penetrate these clouds and it is by radio observations that the overall structure of the Galaxy has been mainly determined.

Twelve[5] billion years ago our Galaxy was not at all like it is at the present time; it was an enormous mass of hydrogen gas hanging tenuously in space. It was roughly spherical in shape, and it was slowly rotating. In some way, not completely understood but certainly involving gravitational contraction, this mass of gas became separated from the rest of the universe. In regions of low turbulence and high density, stars formed from some of the gas, and as they condensed and contracted, their gravitational potential energy was converted into internal thermal energy and into radiant heat and light. After a few tens of millions of years, stars stop contracting and settle down for a relatively long period, constant in size like our sun, during which they emit light uniformly and steadily, again like our sun. How did this stability come about? Where did the energy come from, after contraction and the release of gravitational energy stopped?

Again for the answers we must turn to the nuclear laboratory. There we find that with particle accelerators we can cause pairs of deuterons, the heavy hydrogen nuclei with a mass of two units, to fuse into helium nuclei with a mass of four units. This process is called *fusion*. Several steps are required, but we can produce helium nuclei one at a time with our accelerators. In spite of the valiant efforts of scientists throughout the world—in Russia, in England and in the United States— no one has been able to produce a *self-sustaining* fusion process.

Why should anyone want to do so? The answer lies in the fact that all the masses we have quoted have been approximate. The two deuterons together have slightly greater mass than the helium nucleus they form, and when the fusion occurs, the excess mass is converted into energy. By Einstein's famous equation, one obtains the energy released by multiplying the excess mass by the velocity of light, once and then once again.

---

[5] It is generally agreed that the birth of the Galaxy took place 7 to 15 billion years ago. My own best estimate is 12 billion years ago.

Thus a large amount of energy results from the small change in mass, and if the fusion process could be made self-sustaining, as is the fission process in reactors, then we could burn as fuel the heavy hydrogen which forms a part of all sea water. We would have a source of energy sufficient for all mankind forever. The unsolved problem lies in the fact that the nuclear *burning* must take place at such high temperature that we cannot build a furnace which will confine and contain the fuel.

The fusion problem has been solved in stars. Because of their size, stars contain a sufficient amount of material so that they can confine nuclear fuel gravitationally, sustain fusion processes and shine on the energy that comes from these processes. Most importantly, we shall see that stars can fuse protons, the nuclei of ordinary hydrogen into helium and do not require the very rare heavy hydrogen as fuel. Moreover, in the star's early stages of contraction the stellar material is heated until the nuclear processes are triggered by the high temperature. The release of the nuclear energy adds to the violent internal motions, and the contraction of the star is stopped with a delicate balance resulting between inwardly directed gravitational forces and outwardly directed thermal pressure.

As successive nuclear processes take place, the composition of a star changes and the star is said to evolve as its internal structure and external appearance vary in response to these composition changes. More about this anon. It is essential in the point of view of stellar synthesis that instabilities arise during the evolution and aging of a star that return the transmuted material to interstellar space. It is there mixed with the uncondensed hydrogen gas in the Galaxy so that it is available for condensation into second- and later-generation stars. The general state of affairs in this "equilibrium" between stars and the interstellar gas and dust is illustrated in figure 3.

Stellar nucleosynthesis demands that there exists this interchange of material between stars and the interstellar medium of gas and dust. The stars are the nuclear furnaces; the space between is the site of the mixing and dilution which result in the average abundance distribution over fairly large astronomical regions. Observations confirm that matter is given

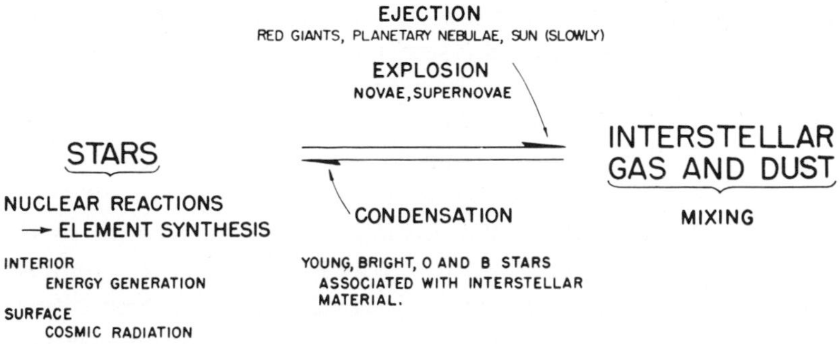

EJECTION

RED GIANTS, PLANETARY NEBULAE, SUN (SLOWLY)

EXPLOSION

NOVAE, SUPERNOVAE

STARS   **INTERSTELLAR**
                                                       GAS AND DUST

NUCLEAR REACTIONS
→ ELEMENT SYNTHESIS   CONDENSATION   MIXING

INTERIOR   YOUNG, BRIGHT, O AND B STARS
   ENERGY GENERATION   ASSOCIATED WITH INTERSTELLAR
                             MATERIAL.
SURFACE
   COSMIC RADIATION

Fig. 3. Transfer of material between stars and interstellar gas and dust. Synthesis of elements occurs in the stars, and mixing to yield the relative cosmic abundance of the elements occurs in interstellar space. Mechanisms for the transfer as observed astronomically are indicated.

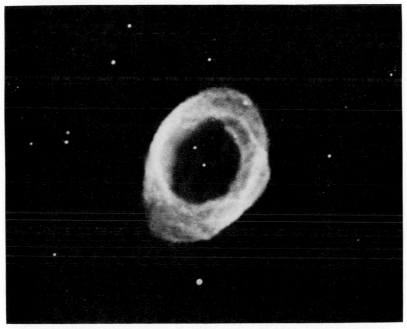

Fig. 4. The "Ring" planetary nebula in *Lyra* showing the spherical shell of gas which is moving away from the central star and was presumably ejected by it. The off-center star within the ring is a field star. (*Mount Wilson and Palomar Observatories.*)

off by stars, both slowly and explosively, and that new stars are continually forming from the interstellar material. Giant stars lose mass at a fairly substantial rate; even our sun slowly ejects matter into space. The planetary nebulae, such as that shown in figure 4, show spherical shells moving away from a central star. Projected on our line of sight through the telescope, such a shell gives the appearance of a gigantic "smoke ring." The most spectacular instabilities in stars result in the novae and supernovae that are observed to flare up suddenly in the sky and then die away in brightness. In the case of novae, a mass loss of the order of one-tenth to one per cent can suddenly occur after which the star involved returns in most cases to approximately its original luminosity. Novae can reoccur. In supernova explosions, all or a substantial fraction of the mass of what is presumed to have been a star is ejected with high velocity into space. I shall discuss the puzzling riddle of the nature of supernovae in the next lecture.

In all these cases, ranging from slow to catastrophic mass loss, we see astronomical evidence that material is transferred from the star to the interstellar medium. If material from the deep interior of the star is involved in the ejection or explosion, then the new elements produced by nuclear burning in this material will be mixed into the interstellar medium. This nuclear burning could have taken place during the previous sedentary history of the star as energy was steadily generated and emitted as light or at a greatly accelerated rate during the final explosive stage. In any case the interstellar medium becomes increasingly contaminated with the debris from past stellar mass losses as the Galaxy ages. Thus there is good observational evidence to believe that new stars which continue to form from the interstellar medium will not consist solely of the primordial hydrogen but also of material enriched in other elements by the addition of nuclear debris from previous generations of stars.

The reverse process to the breakup of stars, the formation of new stars, also has substantial observational confirmation, albeit somewhat indirect. There are stars in the heavens so bright for their known mass that even nuclear processes cannot have kept them shining for more than a few million years. They are thus much younger than the sun and the Galaxy. The bright stars are "young stars," and since they occur only in regions observed to be populated with relatively large amounts of gas, it is reasonable to assume that they condensed from the interstellar material. These "bright" stars often beautifully illuminate the remaining gas and dust near them, as seen in figures 5, 6 and 7.

Consider the very bright star seen just above the tall column of gas and dust in the photograph of the nebulosity in the constellation *Monoceros* shown in figure 7. The nebulosity is called the *Madonna Nebula* for obvious reasons. Note the light from the top of the column. It is scattered light originally emitted by the bright star but absorbed and re-emitted by atoms in the column. Now the very bright star is approximately 10,000 times as luminous as the sun but it is only about

Fig. 5. The Lagoon Nebula in *Sagittarius* showing a region in the Galaxy where bright, young stars have recently formed from interstellar gas and dust. The remaining gas and dust are illuminated by these stars. (*Mount Wilson and Palomar Observatories.*)

FIG. 6. The Orion Nebula showing bright, young stars embedded in interstellar gas and dust. (*Mount Wilson and Palomar Observatories.*)

10 times as massive. Thus it is consuming its nuclear fuel 1,000 times faster than the sun and its lifetime can be expected to be only a thousandth that of the sun. The sun's present age is thought to be 4.5 billion years and it is believed that it will remain in much its present state for another 5 or 6 billion

Fig. 7. Bright young stars in *Monoceros* which illuminate the gas and dust remaining after their formation. (*Mount Wilson and Palomar Observatories.*)

years. At the age of 10 billion years the sun will change markedly. It will probably explode as a supernova but it may quietly but quickly become a dwarf star. In any case 10 billion years is a good round number for the lifetime of the sun as a normal star. This tells us then the maximum lifetime

of the bright star in *Monoceros*—a mere 10 million years, very
short compared to the age of the Galaxy. Thus sometime
within the last 10 million years this star was formed presumably
from gas and dust similar to that remaining in the nebulosity.

In regions of no gas and dust, there are few great bright stars;
only old stars of low mass, low central temperatures, and low
nuclear reaction rates are found there. They are the slow
burners from the original and succeeding condensations that
cleaned up the vicinity in which they are located. The galactic
rotation has acted to concentrate the gas and dust into the
spiral arms of the equatorial plane of the Galaxy. Under the
influence of the rotation and the galactic gravitational attraction, both stars and the interstellar matter execute generalized
Keplerian orbits in which they are carried through the galactic
equatorial plane from time to time. Atomic collisions retard
the motions of the gas but not of the stars, and thus the gas
accumulates in the galactic plane, where it forms the spiral
arms and the bright, young stars found predominantly in these
arms. For example, the central stars of planetary nebulae
(fig. 4) will be stripped of their gaseous, external clouds as
they pass through the galactic equator. The older stars are
found throughout the galaxy in what is termed the galactic
"halo" and in general have much higher velocities than the
stars in the spiral arms. Stars of intermediate age and velocity
are formed in a region called the galactic disk which is somewhat thicker than that containing the spiral arms. Stars which
populate these various regions are referred to as halo population (originally called population II), arm population (originally called population I), and disk population (differentiated
only recently).

PURE HYDROGEN BURNING

The process of gravitational contraction of a protostar containing only hydrogen leads to a temperature and density
rise in the interior and to a gradient in these quantities such
that the temperature and density are highest at the center of
the star and drop off rapidly to relatively low values at the
stellar surface. When the central temperature reaches 10^7

H- BURNING
THE FUSION OF ORDINARY HYDROGEN
IN MAIN SEQUENCE STARS (THE SUN)

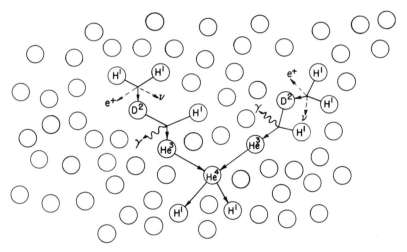

OVERALL RESULT: 4 HYDROGEN NUCLEI → HELIUM NUCLEUS

ENERGY RELEASE = 100 MILLION KILOWATT– HOURS
PER POUND CONVERTED

Fig. 8. Schematic representation of the fusion of hydrogen into helium by the *p-p* chain which occurs in main sequence stars of one solar mass or less. Density: 10^2 gm/cm³. Temperature: 10^7 degrees K.

degrees absolute and the density reaches 100 g/cm³, the hydrogen begins to interact through the so-called direct proton-proton chain which consists in part of the reactions shown in figure 8. The reactions proceed with the emission of large amounts of energy even when the reactants have relatively low energies. The reaction products rapidly lose their large energies by atomic (not nuclear) collisions, and thus the reactions are not reversed. In Lecture II I shall discuss further elaborations of the proton-proton chain.

The steps in the proton-proton chain illustrated in figure 8 can be described in the following manner. In a violent collision two protons (H^1) fuse together to form the deuteron (D^2) with the emission of a neutrino (ν) and a positron (e^+). The neutrino escapes directly from the star because it interacts

only very infrequently with other forms of matter. The positron soon collides with an electron, and both are annihilated
with the appearance of radiant energy. The deuteron eventually
collides with a proton with the formation of a nucleus of
helium with a mass of three units (He^3) and the appearance
of more radiant energy. The He^3 does not interact with protons
except through the process of nuclear scattering in which the
He^3 and H^1 change their individual energies with no change
in their combined energy. Such scatterings play no direct
role in nucleosynthesis or energy generation. The deuterons
are very rare since they react with protons to form He^3 just
as fast as they are produced and thus interactions between
He^3 and D^2 are very rare indeed. As a consequence the He^3
builds up in abundance until pairs of He^3 nuclei interact to
form the common form of helium with a mass of four units
(He^4) plus two protons.

Thus we see that six protons interact in a fairly complicated
way to form He^4 with the reappearance of two protons. The
overall result is the conversion of four protons into the He^4-
nucleus. Of the four electrons which originally balanced the
charge on the four protons, two were annihilated by positrons
and two remain to balance the double charge of He^4. Two
neutrinos escape for each He^4 produced. It is important to
realize that the detailed processes just described are not theoretical pipe dreams. With the exception of the initial proton-
proton fusion all of these reactions have been observed in the
nuclear laboratory and the rates at which they proceed have
been carefully measured. The proton-proton fusion rate is too
low to be detected experimentally but it can be calculated
quite accurately from the rate of proton-proton scattering with
which the fusion process competes and from the rate of other
beta-decay processes in which positrons and neutrinos are
emitted.

Laboratory measurements also reveal the amount of energy
released in the various steps in the proton-proton chain. The
overall energy release corresponds to the difference in initial
and final masses multiplied by the velocity of light squared
as is well known from Einstein's equation $E = Mc^2$, E being
the energy released when mass M is destroyed. The velocity of

light is designated by c. Since c is equal to 3×10^{10} centimeter per second, its square is equal to 9×10^{20} centimeter^2 per second^2. The metric energy unit, the erg can be expressed as gram centimeter^2 per second^2 and so $c^2 = 9 \times 10^{20}$ ergs per gram. This is to say that each gram converted results in the release of 9×10^{20} ergs. Now the four protons and the two annihilated electrons have a mass 0.7 per cent greater than that of the He^4 nucleus *from laboratory measurements*. Thus the conversion of one gram of hydrogen into helium results in the release of approximately 6×10^{18} ergs of energy. Translated into practical units this means that one pound of hydrogen yields 100 million kilowatt-hours of energy when converted into 0.993 pounds of helium. This is one more example of the fact that nuclear burning is prodigal in energy release compared to chemical burning—prodigal enough to keep the sun shining for 10 billion years before its interior hydrogen will have been consumed.

From the standpoint of stellar nucleosynthesis, the proton-proton chain is important because it is a mechanism by which *pure hydrogen* can be converted into helium. The "big bang" production of helium is not needed in principle. However, the proper question is this: Has there been enough helium production in stars? The answer cannot be given at the present time. I do not believe that ordinary stellar activity will suffice but in my last lecture I will discuss the possible copious production of helium in the explosion of super-massive stars.

The fusion of protons into helium can occur in stars even though protons are all positively charged and mutually repel each other. As a matter of fact, on classical Newtonian mechanics, the fusion cannot occur, because even at stellar temperatures the protons do not have sufficient relative velocities to overcome their mutual repulsion. Sir Arthur Eddington, who proposed hydrogen fusion as the source of energy in stars in 1920, gave a magnificent answer to those who criticized him on classical grounds:

> We do not argue with the critic who urges that the stars are not hot enough for this process; we tell him to go and find a hotter place.

Eddington's critics were saved from their classical fate by modern quantum mechanics, which governs the behavior of atomic particles and permits fusion to occur even when it is "impossible" on Newtonian mechanics. This matter is one of degree. Electrostatic repulsions between positively charged nuclei retard the nuclear interactions between them but do not prevent them entirely at low temperatures and low relative velocities.

The above quotation from Eddington is taken from his address to the British Association for the Advancement of Science at Cardiff, Wales. Because it is so relevant to the subject at hand and so prophetic, I cannot refrain from quoting from this address once again:

> If, indeed, the sub-atomic energy in the stars is being freely used to maintain their great furnaces, it seems to bring a little nearer to fulfillment our dream of controlling this latent power for the well-being of the human race— or for its suicide.

Pure Helium Burning

Stars which live and shine from energy generated through the process $4H^1 \rightarrow He^4$ fall in a luminosity-color classification called the "main sequence." However, as the hydrogen in the central regions of the star is exhausted, the star ceases to be homogeneous in composition throughout its interior and will move, or "evolve," off the main sequence. The conversion of hydrogen "fuel" into helium "ash" occurs in the core of the star because the temperature and density are highest there. Judging from astrophysical observations, it appears that the reaction product, helium, is mixed with the outer envelope, still hydrogen, with extreme difficulty. Thus, a core of helium develops and gradually increases in size as more and more hydrogen is converted. Because of greater electrostatic repulsions, the doubly charged He^4 does not burn at 10^7 degrees or even at considerably higher temperatures, and so energy generation ceases except in a thin shell surrounding the helium core. This shell now contains the hottest hydrogen in the star. It has been estimated that the shell temperatures reach 3×10^7

degrees, while the density is of the order of 10 gm/cm^3. In the central regions, the nuclear hydrogen furnace goes out for lack of fuel, and one would expect from ordinary experience with furnaces that the temperature would drop. But this is not at all the case in stars because of their great potential gravitational energy. The helium in the core begins to contract and its temperature rises as gravitational energy is converted into kinetic energy.

This "anomalous" behavior of stars is not all pure conjecture, for the sudden rise in temperature of the core also heats up the envelope, which expands enormously and increases the surface area of the star. The increased area means that energy can be radiated at a lower surface temperature, and thus the surface reddens in color. Larger in area and redder in color than main-sequence stars of the same luminosity, these stars are aptly called the "red giants" by astronomers.

Eventually the helium in the core reaches temperatures ($\sim 10^8$ degrees) and densities ($\sim 10^5$ gm/cm^3) at which Coulomb repulsions should no longer critically inhibit nuclear processes between two helium nuclei. What these processes might be constituted for a long time the Gordian knot of nuclear astrophysics. Two helium nuclei, upon interacting, might be expected to form Be^8. However, as noted previously, no nucleus of mass 8 exists in nature, and from this, early investigators inferred that it must be unstable. Shortly after World War II, this was confirmed in quantitative measurements of the Be^8 decay at Los Alamos and the California Institute of Technology. In both laboratories it was found that when Be^8 was produced artificially in nuclear reactions, it promptly broke up into two alpha particles. However, the energy of breakup was found to be relatively small, slightly less than 100 keV. With this last fact in mind, Salpeter of Cornell University then pointed out that, although hot interacting helium in a star will not produce a stable Be^8 nucleus, it will produce, at 10^8 degrees and 10^5 gm/cm^3, a small but real concentration of Be^8 as a result of the equilibrium between the formation and breakup processes. Now, nuclei are found in the laboratory to capture alpha particles with the emission of energy in the form of gamma radiation. Salpeter pointed out that the Be^8 should behave similarly and that if, after its formation from two alpha particles, it collided with a third, the well-known stable nucleus C^{12} should be formed. Because of the low equilibrium concentration of the Be^8, about 1 part in 10 billion at 100 million degrees, Hoyle emphasized that the Be^8 capture process had better be a very rapid one, or a "resonant" reaction in nuclear parlance. Experiments at Stanford, Brookhaven, and the California Institute of Technology have shown that this is the case. It has been possible to show that there exists an excited state of the C^{12} nucleus at 7.656 MeV, with almost the exact energy of excitation and other properties which Hoyle predicted that it must have in order to serve as a thermal resonance for the formation of C^{12} from Be^8 and He^4 in stars.

Thus, there now exists a reasonable experimental basis for the two-state process by which three alpha particles in the hot dense cores of red giant stars can synthesize carbon, bypassing the intervening elements lithium, beryllium, and boron. This process is indicated schematically in figure 9. The over-all process can, in fact, be looked upon as an equilibrium between three helium nuclei and the excited carbon $C^{12}*$, with occasional irreversible leakage out of the equilibrium to the ground state of C^{12}. In reaction notation, we have

$$3He^4 \rightleftarrows C^{12}* \rightarrow C^{12}.$$

The C^{12} frequently captures a helium nucleus to form O^{16} before the helium is exhausted. In extreme cases this results in the over-all process $4He^4 \rightarrow O^{16}$. A small amount of Ne^{20} is produced in the capture of He^4 by O^{16}. In stars, there is no difficulty at mass 5 and the difficulty at mass 8 has been surmounted. When the central conditions in a red giant reach 10^8 degrees and 10^5 gm/cm^3, the helium begins to burn and energy is released. Because of the small fraction, 0.07 per cent, of mass converted into energy in the above process, the red giant star is not stabilized for any long period after the onset of the helium burning. The major release in nuclear energy comes in the first process, $4H^1 \rightarrow He^4$. In any case,

THE FUSION OF HELIUM IN
RED GIANT STARS

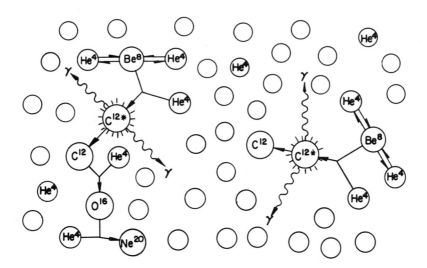

DENSITY : 10^5 GRAMS PER CM^3
TEMPERATURE : 1.3×10^8 DEGREES KELVIN

FIG. 9. Schematic representation of the fusion of helium to form C^{12} which occurs in red giant stars. Density: 10^5 gm/cm³. Temperature: 1.3×10^8 degrees K.

however, the astronomical evidence indicates that the trend toward catastrophic internal temperatures is stopped and the evolutionary track reversed. Stars that become unstable at this point will eject unburnt hydrogen and helium and the synthesized carbon, oxygen and neon into interstellar matter. Others which remain stable will continue the synthesis process.

*   *   *   *

The first essentials of stellar nucleosynthesis have now been told. I shall discuss the formation of still heavier elements beyond carbon, oxygen and neon in the following lectures. In this lecture we have seen how it is possible in stars for hydrogen to fuse into helium and for helium to fuse into carbon, some oxygen, and a little neon. The story is not too greatly different from the ideas of the ancient Greeks to whom I referred at the start of this lecture. Consider a quotation from the Greek philosopher, Simplicius, of the sixth century A.D. in his analysis of the ideas of another Greek philosopher, Leucippus, of the fifth century B.C., generally considered to be the originator of the theory of atomism:

> They (atoms) move in the void and catching each other up jostle together, and some recoil in any direction that may chance, and others become entangled with one another in various degrees according to the symmetry of their shapes and sizes and positions and order, and they remain together and thus the coming into being of composite things is effected.

It might seem that we have not learned very much in the last 2,500 years. In this lecture, however, I have tried to emphasize one important feature of our present-day science which distinguishes it from that of the Greeks. Astronomers now make observations with powerful telescopes. Nuclear physicists perform experiments with powerful accelerators. The concepts of modern-day nuclear astrophysics are rooted in experimental and observational evidence which can be tested and retested. It is the interplay of theory with experiment on the one hand and observation on the other which sharpens and clarifies our knowledge of the world about us.

And now permit me to pass along one final thought in concluding this first lecture. My major theme has been that all of the elements heavier than helium, and perhaps the helium too, have been synthesized in stars. Let me remind you that your bodies consist for the most part of these heavier elements. Thus it is possible to say that you and your neighbor and I, each one of us and all of us, are truly and literally a little bit of stardust.

II. Neutrons, Neutrinos, Red Giants, and Supernovae

Electrically neutral particles play an important role in the building of the elements—so we found in Lecture I, although that lecture primarily emphasized charged particle reactions. These uncharged particles are the neutron, the neutrino and their antiparticles. The properties of the neutron make it easy to detect and study in the laboratory even though it is radioactive with a half-life of only twelve minutes. It has about the same mass as the proton which, it will be recalled, is the nucleus of the atom of ordinary hydrogen.

The neutron behaves like a tiny top, just as do the proton and other nuclei, and it is said to have intrinsic angular momentum or *spin*[1] associated with its rotation. It has a measurable magnetic moment and thus behaves like a tiny magnet. Magnetism arises from the motion of electric charges. How then can the neutral neutron with no net charge have magnetic properties? It would take us far afield to describe the entire matter. Suffice it to say that the neutron is probably made up of still more fundamental particles having both positive and negative charge. The charges balance to give a net charge of zero but the motions of the charges are such that their magnetic contributions do not cancel and consequently the neutron is magnetic.

Like the proton the neutron interacts strongly with other nuclei. In fact, at low energy and low temperature the neutron interacts much more readily than the proton since it is not

---

[1] In quantitative terms this spin is exactly equal to one-half the basic unit of angular momentum used in physics. The unit of angular momentum is related to h, the quantum constant introduced by Planck and named for him. In fact, the unit is just Planck's constant divided by 2π and the spins of the proton and neutron are equal to $h/4\pi$.

electrostatically repelled by other nuclei. The effective target cross sections for the capture of slow neutrons by nuclei were found to be quite large in terms of nuclear dimensions by early investigators. At Los Alamos, throughout World War II, they were said to be "as big as a barn." The word *barn*[2] caught on; it was set equal to 10^{-24} square centimeters and made the unit of nuclear cross sections. It seems a very small target area in the macroscopic world but it is large indeed in the nuclear world.

The *antineutron* does not occur naturally in our part of the universe except in secondaries produced by the cosmic radiation. Antineutrons have been produced in the laboratory and their properties have been studied. They are similar to neutrons in some ways. They have exactly the same charge (zero), exactly the same mass and exactly the same spin. They differ from neutrons in one important respect: their magnetic moment is equal in magnitude but opposite in sign relative to the direction of their axis of rotation. Antineutrons *annihilate* neutrons with the emission of energy equivalent to the rest mass of the two particles multiplied by the velocity of light squared. We can infer that antineutrons interact with anti-nuclei just as neutrons interact with nuclei: they will usually be captured into bound states with the emission of binding energy equivalent to about one per cent of their rest mass energy. Antineutrons interact violently with ordinary nuclei since they annihilate one of the neutrons which serve as nucleons in the nucleus in question. This nucleus is usually disrupted by the great energy release of the annihilation process. Similarly neutrons interact violently with antinuclei.

Properties of the Neutrino and Antineutrino

Neutrinos and antineutrinos are similar to neutrons and antineutrons in that they have zero electric charge and one-half

---

[2] The word originated with M. G. Holloway and C. P. Baker in 1942 while engaged in a national defense project at Purdue University.

unit of spin.[3] There the resemblance ends. Neutrinos and antineutrinos have zero rest mass and zero magnetic moment and they do not interact strongly with nuclei or antinuclei. Thus they are unaffected by electric, magnetic, and the so-called *strong* nuclear fields. They are acted upon by gravity only through their kinetic energy of motion. How then do they interact with other particles in such a way that they play a role in the physical universe and in such a way that we can detect them? The answer is that they do interact through what is called the *weak* nuclear field. This field is thought to be a universal one—that is, it applies to all known particles. However, it is so weak compared to the other natural interactions that it can be ignored under many circumstances for particles which share these other interactions. For neutrinos and anti-neutrinos this interaction is paramount—it alone determines their emission, absorption, and scattering. Pauli postulated that neutrinos and antineutrinos were emitted in nuclear beta-decay along with positrons and electrons in order to conserve energy and momentum. Fermi showed that a very short range field acting between the neutron and proton and these four "light weight" particles gave theoretical results in accord with the observations on the beta-decay emission.

In 1935 Fermi made this a weak field since beta-decays are observed to be very slow compared to other nuclear transformations. In general, weak fields produce slow transformations; strong fields operate rapidly. Compare the weak interaction lifetime of the neutron, 12 minutes, with the time,

----

[3] Neutrinos were postulated in 1930 by Wolfgang Pauli before the discovery of the neutron. Pauli originally called neutrinos by the name neutron. It was Fermi who gave them the name neutrino, or "the little neutron" in *Italian,* when what is now called the neutron was discovered by James Chadwick in 1932. In this lecture I shall not discuss the recently discovered (1965) massless, chargeless particles which are associated with muons (heavy electrons) in much the same way that neutrinos are associated with ordinary electrons. They probably have little to do with the problems with which we are concerned but one can never be sure. These newly discovered particles are informally called *neutrettos* and *antineutrettos* by many physicists. I hope the name sticks.

10^{-21} seconds, with which it is ejected by the strong nuclear interaction from He^5 or Li^5. Frederick Reines and Clyde Cowan of Los Alamos put on the capstone by showing that antineutrinos from the Savannah River Atomic Reactor could be absorbed in hydrogen even though they trapped only one in a billion-billion of these elusive particles which traversed their detector. What they really detected was the energy released in subsequent interactions by the neutron and positron produced when a proton in the hydrogen atom captured one of the antineutrinos.

The absorption of neutrinos has not yet been detected but physicists are confident that this will eventually be accomplished. This leads us naturally to two questions. One, why do we need both neutrinos and antineutrinos to describe what happens in nature? After all, the photon,[4] also with zero rest mass and charge, is its own antiparticle. Two, how do we tell the neutrino and antineutrino apart? The photon can readily be distinguished from these particles since it takes part in electromagnetic interactions. When electrons change energy states in atoms and when nucleons change energy states in nuclei, photons are emitted but not neutrinos or antineutrinos. The nucleons[5] themselves must change for the latter to be emitted or absorbed.

How to Tell the Antineutrinos from the Neutrinos[6]

Let us start on the answer to our two questions by calling the neutral particle emitted with the positron in beta-decay

---

[4] The photon is the elementary particle or "quantum" of electromagnetic radiations such as radio, light, x-rays and gamma rays. The photon is exceptional (but not unique) in that it is its own antiparticle, that is, the photon and antiphoton are identical. To put it in another way the electromagnetic radiations from systems of antimatter are identical with those from matter and thus can be absorbed by matter. We shall have no trouble detecting light signals from an antigalaxy but we shall not be able to show that it consists of antimatter rather than matter on the basis solely of the light received from it.

[5] Certain other elementary particles with which we are not concerned can also emit and absorb neutrinos and antineutrinos.

[6] This question can be generalized in any way desired by the reader. For example, how does one tell the *antibirds* from the birds? In this case one

the *neutrino* and that emitted with the electron the *antineutrino*. Then, on very general grounds arising from the overall
symmetry of the weak interactions, the neutrino will be emitted
when an electron is captured and vice versa, and the antineutrino will be emitted when a positron is captured and vice
versa. Now introduce the symbols: p^+ = proton (the superscript + is commonly omitted in designating the proton), n =
neutron, e^+ = positron or positive electron, e^- = electron,
ν = neutrino and $\bar{\nu}$ = antineutrino. Remember that p and n
represent protons and neutrons in nuclei, not just in the free
state. Then these weak beta-decay processes can be written
symbolically as follows:

$$p^+ \rightarrow n + e^+ + \nu \qquad \text{positron radioactivity}$$
$$n \rightarrow p^+ + e^- + \bar{\nu} \qquad \text{electron radioactivity}$$
$$e^- + p^+ \rightarrow n + \nu \qquad \text{electron capture}$$
$$\nu + n \rightarrow p^+ + e^- \qquad \text{neutrino capture}$$
$$e^+ + n \rightarrow p^+ + \bar{\nu} \qquad \text{positron capture}$$
$$\bar{\nu} + p^+ \rightarrow n + e^+ \qquad \text{antineutrino capture}$$

Note that these reactions all conserve electric charge; that is,
the net charge on one side of the arrow is equal to that on the
other side. Note, too, that the third process can be derived
from the first by transposing the positron from the right side
to the left side and transforming it into its antiparticle, the
electron. Such transformations, upon transposition, are dictated
by very basic physical laws applying to all processes, not just
beta-decay. Similarly, the fourth process can be obtained from
the second by transposing the antineutrino from the right side
to the left side and changing it into its antiparticle, the neutrino.

All of the above is fine and dandy and follows the general
"conservation" laws that are obeyed by these processes. It is
easy to see that we need both electrons and positrons: they

---

method of procedure is quite clear. First, you have to catch your antibird,
then . . .

have opposite charges (and magnetic moments) and are certainly not identical. But could not $v \equiv \bar{v}$? Let us return to perusal of the reactions above. We note that the fifth process can be obtained from transposition and transformation of the electron in the second and that the sixth is just the reverse of the fifth. Thus antineutrinos produced in electron radioactivity *must* be absorbable in hydrogen with the production of neutrons and positrons. This is just what Reines and Cowan proved at Savannah River.

But now consider the second and the fourth processes. If neutrinos and antineutrinos are identical, $v \equiv \bar{v}$, then the neutral particles from electron radioactivity in the Savannah River reactor should induce proton and electron emission by the interaction with neutrons in nuclei. This was shown *not* to be the case by Raymond Davis, Jr., of the Brookhaven National Laboratory. Davis used heavy chlorine nuclei, $_{17}\mathrm{Cl}^{37}$, as targets near the reactor and showed that radioactive argon $_{18}\mathrm{Ar}^{37}$, which results if a neutron in $_{17}\mathrm{Cl}^{37}$ changes to a proton, was not produced within the limits of his detection sensitivity. Since neutrinos are thought to be emitted when artificially produced $_{18}\mathrm{Ar}^{37}$ captures an electron to form $_{17}\mathrm{Cl}^{37}$, on the general grounds of the reversibility of processes it is believed that neutrinos would produce $_{18}\mathrm{Ar}^{37}$ from $_{17}\mathrm{Cl}^{37}$. Davis showed that antineutrinos do not. Thus neutrinos and antineutrinos cannot be identical.

In what way then do they differ? Detailed observations of the beta decays show that the answer lies in their spin orientations relative to their direction of motion as shown in figure 10. Nuclear experimentalists are able to measure the linear momentum and the angular momentum or spin of the charged particles involved in beta decay. Two basic physical laws governing processes on which no external forces or torques are exerted are: the net linear momentum cannot change and the net angular momentum cannot change. Thus the experimentalist can calculate the linear and angular momentum of neutrinos and antineutrinos from the net deficiency in these quantities measured for the easily observed charged particles. Figure 10 shows the results of the observations and calculations.

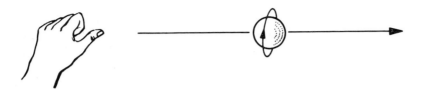

THE LEFT-HANDED NEUTRINO

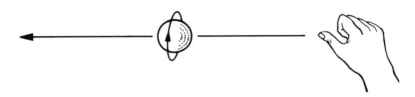

THE RIGHT-HANDED ANTINEUTRINO

FIG. 10. The helicity or handedness of the neutrino and the antineutrino.

The neutrino always spins relative to its direction of motion as given by its linear momentum in just the way that a left-handed screw advances. In other words, if the thumb of the left hand is pointed along the direction of motion the fingers indicate the direction of rotation. On the other hand the antineutrino is right-handed. The magnitudes of the spins are found to be the same $(h/4\pi)$ but the spins of the neutrinos and anti-neutrinos are said to be 100 per cent polarized in opposite directions relative to their linear motion. Ordinary electrons can be polarized in this sense in either direction. A beam of electrons from a hot filament contains an equal number spin-ning in each direction relative to their direction of motion. The net polarization is zero. However, electrons emitted in beta decay are found to be polarized in the left-handed sense to the maximum extent permitted by relativity theory for a particle with non-zero rest mass. Similarly the positrons are found to be right-handed. The general rule seems to be: what we call particles are left-handed, what we call antiparticles are right-handed.

A Quibble

Unfortunately, in a sense, it is necessary to qualify all of the above statements somewhat. There are those who argue that the observational limits on the experimental results still permit of a different point of view. The neutrino and antineutrino may be identical and it is the basic nature of the weak interaction which determines everything. The negative particle is spun in the left-handed sense by this interaction to the maximum extent possible. The interaction then spins the neutral particle emitted at the same time in the right-handed sense. The positive particle is spun in the right-handed sense and the neutral particle emitted with it is spun in the left-handed sense. The situation is then similar to that for photons which can be emitted with either left-handed or right-handed circular polarization. (The unit of spin for the photon is $h/2\pi$, just twice that for the neutrinos.) This all seems to me to be largely a matter of semantics. Semantics it will certainly be if the neutrinos can be shown to have absolutely zero mass and if the weak interaction is taken to be "pure" in the sense of always distinguishing absolutely between right- and left-handed polarization. At the present time most physicists follow the terminology indicated in figure 10.

The Detection of Solar and Cosmic Neutrinos

Let us turn now to the role played by neutrinos in nuclear processes which generate energy and synthesize new elements in stars. Figure 8 showed that the burning of pure hydrogen produced two neutrinos[7] for each helium nucleus produced. This will always be the case but when the hydrogen is not pure a variety of reactions can lead to the production of helium

---

[7] These are neutrinos not antineutrinos. Antineutrinos are produced by some faraway antisun which burns antihydrogen to form antihelium. The antipeople on a nearby antiplanet probably think that we are thetic. Experts are fairly certain that they use macassars on their antichairs. A most interesting point is this. We shall see in succeeding paragraphs that we can observationally differentiate antineutrinos from neutrinos. Thus in contrast to the result discussed in footnote 4 we shall be able to distinguish an antigalaxy from a galaxy if we are ever able to show that its main sequence stars emit antineutrinos rather than neutrinos.

and neutrinos. Even if a star consists initially of pure hydrogen it will eventually build up He^4 which can itself play a role as a *nuclear catalyst* in the further production of He^4.

The important proton-proton chain processes are indicated in nuclear reaction notation in table 3. Note that the He^4 which is consumed with He^3 to form Be^7 is returned along with a second He^4 in both alternatives in the right-hand set of reactions. The first He^4 serves as a *catalyst* in the production of the second. If a star contains carbon, nitrogen, or oxygen, and if its central temperature is high enough for these elements to interact with hydrogen then another set of reactions shown in table 4 serve to process the hydrogen into helium. The first part of this set was originally known as the CN cycle but the total set is now known as the CNO bi-cycle, since a second cycle is completed when O^{17} goes to N^{14} just as the original cycle is completed when N^{15} returns to C^{12}. Starting with one

TABLE 3

THE PP-CHAIN

$H^1 + H^1 \rightarrow D^2 + e^+ + v$	$Be^7 + e^- \rightarrow Li^7 + v$
$D^2 + H^1 \rightarrow He^3 + \gamma$	$Li^7 + H^1 \rightarrow He^4 + He^4$
$He^3 + He^3 \rightarrow He^4 + H^1 + H^1$	OR
OR	$Be^7 + H^1 \rightarrow B^8 + \gamma$
$He^3 + He^4 \rightarrow Be^7 + \gamma$	$B^8 \rightarrow Be^{8*} + e^+ + v$
	$Be^{8*} \rightarrow He^4 + He^4$

How to read table 3. The first three reactions have been discussed in Lecture I. In the fourth reaction, He^3 and He^4 fuse together to form Be^7, a radioactive isotope of beryllium, with the emission of a gamma ray. The Be^7 usually captures a nearby electron to form Li^7, the heavy stable isotope of lithium, with the emission of a neutrino. The Li^7 interacts with H^1 to form two He^4 nuclei or alpha-particles. Less frequently the Be^7 captures a proton, H^1, to form B^8, a radioactive isotope of boron, which decays to an excited state, Be^{8*}, of the mass-eight beryllium nucleus. This excited nucleus in turn breaks up into two He^4 nuclei. The overall result in all cases is that four protons have been converted into an alpha-particle plus two positrons and two neutrinos or that four protons plus an electron have been converted into an alpha-particle plus one positron and two neutrinos. Note that the He^4 which produces Be^7 originally is eventually re-emitted with a second He^4 nucleus. In this way one He^4 acts as a catalyst to produce a second.

TABLE 4

THE CNO BI-CYCLE

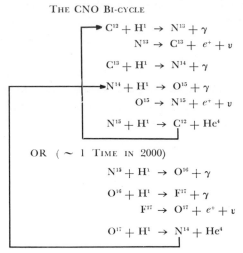

$$C^{12} + H^1 \rightarrow N^{13} + \gamma$$
$$N^{13} \rightarrow C^{13} + e^+ + \upsilon$$
$$C^{13} + H^1 \rightarrow N^{14} + \gamma$$
$$N^{14} + H^1 \rightarrow O^{15} + \gamma$$
$$O^{15} \rightarrow N^{15} + e^+ + \upsilon$$
$$N^{15} + H^1 \rightarrow C^{12} + He^4$$

OR ($\sim$ 1 TIME IN 2000)

$$N^{15} + H^1 \rightarrow O^{16} + \gamma$$
$$O^{16} + H^1 \rightarrow F^{17} + \gamma$$
$$F^{17} \rightarrow O^{17} + e^+ + \upsilon$$
$$O^{17} + H^1 \rightarrow N^{14} + He^4$$

How to read table 4. The light, stable isotope of carbon, C^{12}, captures a proton, H^1, to form radioactive nitrogen, N^{13}, with the emission of a gamma ray. The N^{13} decays to the heavy, stable isotope of carbon, C^{13}, with the emission of a positron and a neutrino. The C^{13} captures a proton to form stable N^{14} which in turn captures a proton to form radioactive oxygen, O^{15}. The O^{15} decays to stable N^{15} with the emission of a second positron and a second neutrino. When the N^{15} reacts with H^1 it almost invariably forms a He^4 nucleus or alpha-particle with C^{12} as the residual nucleus. Thus the original C^{12} is returned and the CN cycle, as it is called, is repeated over and over again. The overall result is always the conversion of four protons into an alpha-particle plus two positrons and two neutrinos. The C^{12}, N^{13}, C^{13}, N^{14}, O^{15}, and N^{15} serve as catalysts. These reactions have all been produced and studied in detail in nuclear laboratories. In about one time in 2000 the N^{15} captures H^1 to form stable oxygen, O^{16} with the emission of a gamma ray. Further reactions transpire and these are left to the reader to decipher. A second cycle occurs and the overall set of reactions is called the CNO bi-cycle.

or more of the isotopes of carbon, nitrogen and oxygen the bi-cycle synthesizes all of the others in fixed proportions depending on the temperature and this fixed mixture catalytically processes hydrogen into helium. This is to say that the total number of CNO nuclei remains unchanged. The initial nuclei are usually C^{12} or O^{16} which were produced in helium burning in previous stars as discussed in Lecture I. We see incidentally that starting with these nuclei the bi-cycle synthesizes C^{13}, N^{14}, N^{15} and O^{17} with the radioactive nuclei

N^{13}, O^{15}, and F^{17} being produced momentarily. It is actually in this way that the stable cases are thought to have been produced in stellar nucleosynthesis.

Any way one looks at tables 3 and 4 it will be found that two neutrinos are produced for every helium nucleus synthesized from four protons. This can be used to calculate in a very general way the number of neutrinos which reach each unit area of the earth's surface every second from the sun. This number is very important to the neutrino astronomer who hopes to detect solar neutrinos. In Lecture I we learned that the conversion of one gram of hydrogen into helium releases 6×10^{18} ergs of energy. There are 1.5×10^{23} helium atoms in each gram. Thus 5×10^4 neutrinos fall on the earth for every erg of energy from the sun. We know from laboratory measurements that only a few per cent of the energy generated in either the proton-proton chain or the CNO bi-cycle is carried away by the neutrinos. Most of it leaves the sun as light. So now all we need is the number of ergs of sunlight falling each second on each square centimeter of the earth's surface. The solar constant, as this number is called, has been the subject of extensive investigation for over fifty years starting with the pioneer investigations of C. G. Abbot and his collaborators at the Smithsonian Astrophysical Observatory in 1913. Measurements of increasing precision over the years have been carried out at the Smithsonian, at the National Bureau of Standards and at the Naval Research Laboratory. In "practical" units the constant is now thought to be 2.00 calories per square centimeter per minute within a few percent error. This is equivalent to 14×10^5 ergs per square centimeter per second. With 5×10^4 neutrinos per erg this means that 7×10^{10} neutrinos fall on each square centimeter of the earth every second.

This seems like a large number but we must remember that neutrinos interact only weakly with matter. Numerically neutrino interactions are only 10^{-19} or one ten billion-billionth as frequent as photon interactions. Thus only one in a billion of the neutrinos originating in the center of the sun is trapped before emerging and only one in ten billion falling on the earth fails to emerge from the other side. It is paradoxical in a way that neutrino astronomers can hope to catch these elusive particles. Their hope lies in the great flux, almost 70 billion neutrinos per square centimeter per second, which fall on the earth *if our present understanding of solar energy generation is correct.*

As a matter of fact, number is not all there is to it. The different types of neutrinos from the proton-proton chain and the CNO bi-cycle are emitted with widely differing energies from 0.4 million electron volts (MeV) maximum for those from $H^1 + H^1$ to 14 MeV maximum for those from the B^8 decay in table 3. This is important since neutrino interaction cross sections increase roughly as the square of the neutrino energy. Thus 14 MeV neutrinos from B^8 are in general detected with 1000 times the probability of 0.4 MeV neutrinos from $H^1 + H^1$.

Actually it turns out that the most advanced technique for neutrino detection has a *threshold* such that it can detect only neutrinos with greater than 0.8 MeV energy. This technique has been developed to a point of very high proficiency by Raymond Davis, Jr., of Brookhaven who has used it to show, as mentioned previously, that neutrinos and antineutrinos are not identical.

Davis uses the reactions

$$Cl^{37}_{terr} + \nu_{solar} \rightarrow Ar^{37}_{radio} + e^-$$

$$Ar^{37}_{radio} + e^-_{terr} \rightarrow Cl^{37}_{exc} + \nu \qquad \text{half-life} \sim 1 \text{ month.}$$

$$Cl^{37}_{exc} \rightarrow Cl^{37}_{nor} + e^-_{Auger}$$

Cl^{37} constitutes 25 per cent of ordinary chlorine. Davis looks for the *radioactive* argon, Ar^{37}, produced when *solar* neutrinos are captured by the *terrestrial* Cl^{37} in large tanks of the cheap cleaning fluids carbon tetrachloride, CCl_4, or perchlorethylene, C_2Cl_4. In his Savannah River experiments Davis used 1000 gallon tanks (fig. 11). In his Brookhaven Neutrino Observatory deep in the Homestake Mine (fig. 12) in South Dakota he is installing a 100,000 gallon tank. The radioactive argon produced by the solar neutrinos is a noble, rare gas and does not unite chemically with the chlorine compounds. He sweeps

FIG. 11. Raymond Davis, Jr. (upper left) making adjustments on his Neutrino Detector under a production reactor at the Savannah River Plant, Aiken, South Carolina. The 1,000-gallon tanks containing a chlorine compound, the helium tank, and the trap for separating radioactive argon from the helium are clearly visible.

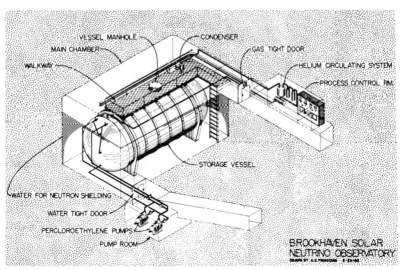

FIG. 12. Schematic drawing of the Brookhaven Solar Neutrino Observatory located in the Homestake Mine, South Dakota.

it out by bubbling helium, also a noble gas, through the liquid and then freezes out the argon by passing the gas mixture through a cold charcoal trap. The small amount of argon gas is then placed in a small, well-shielded, Geiger counter of very low background. The Ar^{37} captures terrestrial electrons to reform Cl^{37} atoms in *excited* states which decay rapidly to *normal* Cl^{37} by ejecting electrons through a mechanism named for the French nuclear physicist, Auger. It is the ionization produced in the counter gas by the Auger electrons which is detected.

In spite of all this experimental complexity Davis will be able to compute, from his measurements of the Ar^{37} radioactivity, the neutrino flux at the earth. The theoretical formulations have been developed meticulously by my colleague, John Bahcall, at California Institute of Technology. Bahcall has shown on the basis of our present ideas of the current sun that Davis should register 6 events per day in his counter. This should be 30 times his background counting rate. Bahcall has shown that the main source of the counts are the high energy neutrinos from B^8 in spite of the fact that present laboratory measurements indicate that B^8 should be produced in only about one in 2,000 of the proton-proton chains. Moreover, this fraction is very sensitive to the temperature of the sun's central regions in which the hydrogen is burning and the neutrinos are being produced. In fact Davis need only measure his counting rate to 50 per cent in order to be able to determine the sun's central temperature to 10 per cent. Neutrinos come directly from the center of the sun and tell us what is happening there; light photons come from the surface and tell us what is happening there. The nuclear physicist is much more interested in the center!

Davis' observations will cost around one-half million dollars. In defense of this outlay by the Atomic Energy Commission, Bahcall presents the following argument. A precision laboratory thermometer costs \$10 and accurately measures up to 1000 °K; the cost is 1 cent per degree. Davis will obtain a figure near 16 million degrees; the cost is 3 cents per degree—not too bad in comparison for a newly developed, one-shot technique.

Neutrinos and antineutrinos almost certainly come to us from other stars and other galaxies—from outer space no less. They come directly with the speed of light and without interference. They are at one and the same time the most reliable and the most reluctant of messengers. Many groups, throughout the world, in deep mines in Utah, South Africa, India, as well as South Dakota have set up equipment to detect solar and cosmic neutrinos. The Case Institute–University of Witwatersrand consortium has already claimed the detection of what are probably neutrettos produced in the earth's atmosphere by the cosmic radiation. Within the next decade we are sure to learn new and startling things about the universe from the newest branch of science—neutrino astronomy.

Before I leave these "little, neutral ones" let me anticipate a question almost always asked as a consequence of the fact that neutrinos and antineutrinos emerge from the stars or supernovae in which they are borne leaving only a small fraction of their companions trapped behind and then cross, as far as we know, the wide expanse of the universe with only infinitesimally small probability of interaction. What happens to neutrinos? There are scientific guesses but none so richly poetical as that by T. S. Eliot in *East Coker*, III (1940):

> O dark dark dark. They all go into the dark,
> The vacant interstellar spaces, the vacant into the vacant.

There are those who would argue otherwise, but Eliot *must* have had neutrinos in mind. The best scientific answer is that due to Steven Weinberg who points out that neutrinos and antineutrinos will be red shifted to low energies by the universal red-shift and will then constitute a "sea" of low energy particles throughout the universe which should be very difficult to detect. Eventually even this will be accomplished.

NEUTRONS AND THE SYNTHESIS OF THE HEAVY ELEMENTS

It will be clear from the foregoing paragraphs that neutrinos play a subtle, indirect role in nucleosynthesis and are of primary importance because they come to us bearing information from the very sites of synthesis activity. It is otherwise with neutrons—these particles play the work-horse role in synthesizing the heavy elements. For this story we must first review and extend the charged particle synthesis described in Lecture I and the first part of this lecture.

Pure hydrogen is converted into helium in first generation main sequence stars through the basic proton-proton chain indicated by the first three reactions of table 3. Helium is converted mostly into carbon and oxygen in first generation red giants. Second generation stars contain some He^4, C^{12}, and O^{16} so that hydrogen burning occurs through the generalized proton-proton chain or through the CNO bi-cycle. In the latter case C^{13}, N^{14}, and N^{15} are synthesized and if instabilities arise these new nuclei are introduced into the interstellar gas from which further generations of stars are to be formed.

The story does not end here. In red giants which remain stable the central helium is eventually exhausted and replaced by the carbon-oxygen "ash" of helium burning. It is characteristic of charged particle processes that the ash has a larger specific nuclear charge than the fuel from which it is produced and will not burn at the temperature which consumes the fuel. The ash from one stage of nuclear burning can become the fuel for the next only if the temperature rises. But this is just what happens when gravitational contraction takes place upon the exhaustion of a given fuel. The contraction raises the temperature and density until the ash of the previous stage ignites and becomes a new source of nuclear energy. The energy generation stops the contraction and a new static period in stellar evolution is begun.

Thus the C^{12}, O^{16} or a mixture of both eventually begins to burn. The result is the production of a number of intermediate mass nuclei among which Ne^{20}, Mg^{24}, Si^{28}, and S^{32} are the most abundant. This is expected from the great nuclear stability of these nuclei with mass number an integral multiple of 4. The great stability is most simply understood in terms of the model in which these nuclei consist of complexes of the highly stable alpha particle. Indeed, these nuclei are the most abundant among the isotopes of the elements neon, magnesium, silicon, and sulfur. In a star which remains stable, the evolutionary process continues. The Coulomb repulsions between nuclei with 10 to 16 times the charge on the proton (neon to sulfur) are very strong and burning no longer proceeds by the simple fusion of the interacting products. Instead, as the temperature rises, a number of the intermediate nuclei are photodisintegrated in the intense high-energy flux of the tail of the Planck distribution with the emission of alpha particles. For example, a Si^{28} nucleus can be broken down into seven alpha particles at temperatures near 3×10^9 degrees. These alpha particles are captured by other nuclei which escape photodisintegration. Thus, another Si^{28} nucleus can capture seven alpha particles to form radioactive nickel, Ni^{56}. The over-all result is $2Si^{28} \rightarrow Ni^{56}$ but the detailed mechanism is not direct fusion but the *alpha-process* (α-process) in which build-up of one nucleus to double its original mass and charge occurs upon the breakdown of another into alpha particles. Ni^{56} decays through radioactive cobalt, Co^{56}, to stable iron, Fe^{56} through the successive capture of two electrons from the plasma continuum in a star with the emission in each capture of a neutrino. Many other nuclei near Fe^{56} from vanadium, V^{50}, to nickel, Ni^{62}, are thought to be produced in this way.

The radioactive captures and photodisintegrations which constitute the α-process were long ago described in another context in a very charming way by Sir Isaac Newton in his *Opticks* (1704):

> The changing of bodies into light, and light into bodies,
> is very conformable to the course of Nature, which seems
> delighted with transmutations.

From the standpoint of nuclear physics, it is clear that the sequence of successive burning of heavier and heavier nuclei through charged-particle reactions should terminate at the iron-group nuclei, which are the most "stable" nuclei in the sense that the internal neutron-proton energies are at a minimum and their binding energies are at a maximum in absolute magnitude. Both heavier and lighter nuclei have higher internal energy content and are less stable in this sense than the iron-group nuclei.

Very high temperatures and great densities will be reached at the production of the iron-group elements. Under these conditions, the rates of all possible reactions will be very great indeed and the situation will be best described in terms of a nuclear equilibrium. This appears to be indeed the case since the relative abundances of the iron-group elements, titanium, vanadium, chromium, manganese, iron, cobalt, and nickel are in good agreement with calculations made by my colleagues, the Burbidges and Fred Hoyle, and myself for the equilibrium distribution at 4 billion degrees Kelvin in temperature and 3 million grams per cubic centimeter in density. This temperature and density are consistent with the stellar conditions leading up to what we called the *equilibrium-process* (*e*-process). It is the *e*-process by which the iron-group elements are synthesized. These elements are overabundant relative to their neighbors at lower and higher atomic numbers. Among them iron is the most abundant. This overabundance can be understood on the basis that enough stars remain stable long enough to develop an iron "ball" in their centers at the end of a long line of energy-generating charged-particle reactions.

The *α*-process and the *e*-process probably occur at a rapidly evolving or even explosive state of stellar evolution. It has been suggested that the collapsing core of a star in its terminal stages as a red giant or in its final catastrophic supernova stage is a possible site for such processes. The collapse of the core is brought about by the fact that no further generation of nuclear energy occurs after the iron-group nuclei are produced. Gravitational contraction takes place unimpeded. The implosion is actually speeded up in the inner regions of the core by the refrigerating action of nuclear processes which transfer some of the iron-group nuclei back into lighter nuclei, mostly He^4 and neutrons, with the absorption of energy.

The implosion of the core removes the underlying support of the envelope material of the star, which contains unevolved nuclear fuel capable of releasing large amounts of energy on being raised to high temperatures. The gravitational collapse of the envelope material does just this. The energy release by the nuclear reactions in the envelope material further raises its temperature, the collapse is reversed by expansion of the material, and all or part of the envelope material and probably even a portion of core material are blown out from the star at high velocity. The result is observed astronomically as the occurrence of a supernova in which a star is observed in a very short interval to flare up to many times its previous luminosity and to eject a large fraction of its mass into space. There will be more to say about this in what follows.

Charged particle reactions terminate with the formation of the iron-group elements. Because of the large, repulsive, electrostatic forces between protons or alpha-particles and the nuclei with charge greater than 30 proton charges, very high temperatures are required for additional synthesis and at these temperatures photodisintegration is actually more effective than charged particle capture. The small relative abundance (0.1 to 1 per cent) of the lightest, "charge-rich" isotopes of the heavy elements attests to the infrequent operation of charged particle reactions in the synthesis of these elements.

On the other hand, neutrons interact rapidly with heavy nuclei at even relatively low temperatures. In fact, neutron reaction cross sections vary roughly as $1/v \sim 1/E^{\frac{1}{2}}$, where v is the velocity and E is the energy of interaction. Since the most probable neutron energy is proportional to the temperature, it will be clear that neutron processes are even more rapid at low temperatures than at high, in marked contrast to charged particle processes. Furthermore, at low energies the only reaction other than elastic scattering which is allowed energetically in most cases is the capture of the neutron. This leads to an increase in atomic weight by one unit, a slow but sure mechanism for the synthesis of heavier and heavier nuclei.

We have previously discussed the difficulties which arise at mass 5 and mass 8 in Gamow's suggestion that neutron capture synthesized all the elements starting with neutron decay during the early stages of the expanding universe. Gamow's basic idea of neutron capture is incorporated in stellar nucleosynthesis, but the difficulties just mentioned are avoided by using charged particle reactions during various stages of stellar evolution to synthesize the elements up to and including the iron group. The key step is $3He^4 \rightleftarrows C^{12*} \rightarrow C^{12}$. Neutron production and capture then serve in the intermediate and terminal stages of stellar evolution as the main line of element synthesis beyond iron. In fact a small fraction, about one-tenth of one per cent, of the abundant iron-group nuclei is used as the "seed" nuclei at the start of the chain of captures. Mass spectroscopy has shown that the chain is unbroken in atomic mass in this region. In fact it is indeed unbroken beyond $A = 8$.

What is the site of the neutron synthesis and what is the source of the neutrons? It is well known from laboratory experiments that proton-induced reactions have fairly high energy thresholds for neutron production. This is to say that p,n-reactions (proton in, neutron out) are endoergic and are thus infrequent at stellar temperatures. On the other hand, certain a,n-reactions (alpha particle in, neutron out) are exoergic, that is, even for low alpha particle energy the neutron is produced with relatively high energy which increases its probability of emission. (Neutron capture varies as $1/v \sim 1/E^{1/2}$, as previously mentioned, but neutron emission varies as $v \sim E^{1/2}$.) One of the most important of these exoergic a,n-reactions involves the nucleus C^{13} as target and O^{16} as product, in detail as follows:

$$C^{13} + He^4 \rightarrow O^{16} + n$$

In more modern notation this is written C^{13} $(an)O^{16}$, where the symbol a is invariably used for the He^4 nucleus when it occurs inside the brackets.

Neutron Reactions in Red Giants; the S-Process

Consider now a second or later generation star which, during its main sequence stage, has converted some C^{12} or O^{16} into C^{13}, as a consequence of hydrogen burning through the CNO bi-cycle. At the termination of the hydrogen burning the C^{13} survives in a region in which the main constituent is He^4. When the star enters the red giant stage with increased central temperature, laboratory measurements by Dr. Cary Davids of the relative reaction rate lead to the conclusion that the C^{13} $(a,n)O^{16}$ reaction occurs even before the further production of C^{12} by $3He^4 \rightleftarrows C^{12*} \rightarrow C^{12}$. Thus neutrons are freed, one for each C^{13} nucleus originally present.

The freed neutrons are preferentially captured by heavy nuclei. If a small number of iron-group nuclei are also contained in the material from which the second or later generation star condensed, then these nuclei will capture the neutrons to build still heavier nuclear forms. The rate of red-giant evolution is relatively slow, and the average interval between neutron captures for a given nucleus can be many years in duration. This interval is long enough for beta-decay processes to occur between neutron captures when a nucleus unstable to electron-antineutrino emission is produced in the capture chain. The neutron captures are *slow* compared to the intervening beta decays, and so this has been designated the *s*-process.

Consider the situation if the synthesis starts with the most probable seed nucleus, Fe^{56}. It captures a neutron to become Fe^{57}, which is stable, and in turn captures a neutron to become Fe^{58}, the heaviest stable isotope of iron. When Fe^{58} captures a neutron, the radioactive nucleus, Fe^{59}, is produced. The half-life of this nucleus is 45 days, so that long before it can capture a neutron in the *s*-process it decays to its daughter product, Co^{59}, the one stable form of cobalt. The Co^{59} leads to radioactive Co^{60} which decays to stable Ni^{60} and so on, and so on. Thus the *s*-process winds through what is called the valley of nuclear stability with the beta decay preventing any attempt to reach those stable nuclei separated from their stable partners "in the valley" by radioactive species. Examples are the tin isotopes, Sn^{122} and Sn^{124}. When the *s*-process reaches Sn^{120}, the next nucleus in the chain is Sn^{121} which is radioactive and decays to Sb^{121}, one of the stable forms of antimony. The antimony leads on to tellurium and beyond and so Sn^{122} and Sn^{124} are by-passed in the *s*-process. This will be brought up again in the sequel.

There are several lines of evidence that the *s*-process has occurred and is even now occurring in red giant stars and I will mention only one. The identification of the unstable element technetium in the spectra of some stars by the late Paul Merrill shows that a supply of neutrons must have been produced and captured not more than several hundred thousand years ago in these stars. Technetium has no stable isotopes and does not occur naturally on earth, but the isotope Tc^{99} is produced in the neutron-capture chain and has a half-life of 2×10^5 years. If it had not been produced in the last several hundred thousand years, it would have decayed to Ru^{99} and no technetium line would be observable. Tc^{97} and Tc^{98} have still longer lifetimes but cannot be produced in the s-process. Promethium has no long-lived isotopes and has not been observed in stellar spectra.

Neutron Reactions in Supernovae; the R-Process

The s-process bypasses many neutron-rich nuclear species, some of which are relatively abundant. How were these by-passed nuclei produced? Furthermore, the s-process terminates at Bi^{209}, the only isotope of bismuth, which is the heaviest non-radioactive nucleus. When Bi^{210} is formed from Bi^{209} it beta-decays to Po^{210} (polonium). This nucleus exhibits natural alpha-radioactivity in which it decays with a half-life of 138 days to Pb^{206} (lead). Successive neutron captures through Pb^{207} and Pb^{208} lead eventually to Pb^{209} which beta-decays to Bi^{209} and the whole cycle is repeated. Each cycle converts 4 neutrons into an alpha-particle, 2 electrons, and 2 antineutrinos. More importantly, this cycle terminates the s-process at the first onset of natural alpha-radioactivity long before the parents Th^{232}, U^{235}, and U^{238} of the natural radioactive series are produced. How were Th^{232}, U^{235}, and U^{238} produced?

The answers to the two questions in the preceding paragraph came from apparently unrelated observations on terrestrial explosions in hydrogen-bomb tests and astronomical explosions in supernova events. We have previously discussed (and given a possible explanation for) the occurrence of a supernova in which a star is observed in a very short time to explode. The primary explosion is known to occur from observations on succeeding nights in less than 24 hours. Furthermore, from the velocity of the ejected gases measured as $\sim 10^8$ cm/sec and assuming initial radii of 10^{10} to 10^{11} cm, it is clear that the radius will double and the average density drop by a factor of 8 in 100 to 1000 sec. This must then be the time scale of the primary explosion, since the nuclear processes with rate proportional to the square of the density presumably will terminate after such a marked decrease in density. The expected decrease in temperature accompanying the expansion will

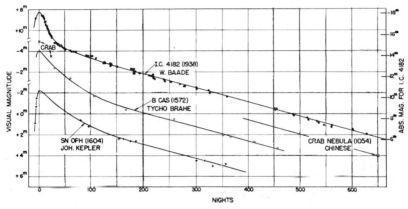

FIG. 13. Light curves of supernovae by Baade. Measures for the supernova IC 4182 are by Baade; those for B Cassiopeiae (1572) and SN Ophiuchi (1604) have been converted by him to the modern magnitude scale from the measures by Tycho Brahe and Kepler. The three points for the supernova of 1054 are uncertain, being taken from the ancient Chinese records. The abscissa gives the number of nights after maximum; the left-hand ordinate gives the apparent magnitude (separate scale for each curve); the points for the Crab nebula belong on the middle scale, i.e., that for B Cassiopeiae. The right-hand ordinate gives the absolute magnitude for IC 4182 derived by using the current distance scale. Compare this figure with the Cf^{254} decay curve as shown in figure 15 but with the Cf^{252} decay shown there reduced by a factor of 50.

only strengthen the argument. Observations on the light curves of supernovae are shown in figure 13. The visual magnitude denoting energy release from the surface is seen at first to rise rapidly as the surface material heats up and then to drop off because of cooling by expansion and radiation. So far, so good. However, after about 50 days, type I supernovae, of which the one which occurred in galaxy IC 4182 in 1938 is an example (fig. 14), show a linearly decreasing magnitude with

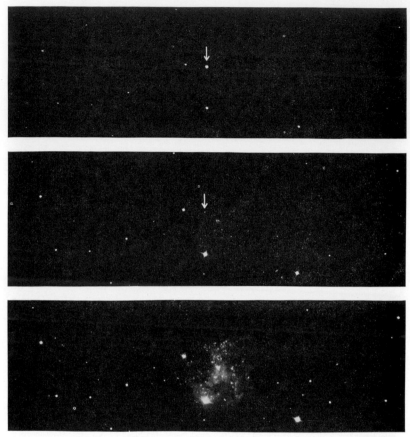

Fig. 14. The supernova in IC 4182, photographed (top) September 10, 1937, at maximum brightness—exposure 20 minutes; (middle) November 24, 1938, about 400 days after maximum—exposure 45 minutes; (bottom) January 19, 1942, about 1,600 days after maximum, when the supernova was too faint to be detected—exposure 85 minutes. Note that the time intervals of the three exposures are different. The galaxy in which the supernova occurred is clearly seen in the bottom photograph. It is not apparent in the two top photographs for which the exposure time was too short. (*Mount Wilson and Palomar Observatories.*)

time. This means an exponentially decreasing luminosity with a half-life which turns out to be 55 ± 1 *nights* (that's when the observations are made!) for IC 4182 and the same value but with somewhat larger probable errors for other cases. It was first suggested by Borst that this behavior, contrary to what is to be expected for further cooling, may be due to the production of radioactivity in the initial explosion and the release of the radioactive energy into the debris with a characteristic half-life near 55 days. Borst suggested Be^7 with a half-life of 53 days, but this had the difficulty that Be^7 decays by electron capture in which the decay energy is that of a neutrino and is thus not converted, even in a stellar mass, into visible radiation. The decay proceeds 10 per cent of the time to an excited state of Li^7, and thus it turns out that about 50 keV of convertible energy is released as gamma radiation per decay. From known supernova luminosities, this required that the entire stellar mass be converted into Be^7 in the explosion, a very unlikely event.

As noted previously, the answer came unexpectedly. In April, 1956, results were finally published of studies by Fields, Seaborg, and collaborators of the radioactivity found in the debris of the first hydrogen-bomb test held near Eniwetok in November, 1952. On chemical analysis the debris revealed that isotopes of the element californium ($Z = 98$) had been produced, and physical measurements showed that these iso-topes decayed by spontaneous fission in which the decay energy has the large value of 200 MeV per event. The decay curve for the mixture of isotopes found in the debris is shown in figure 15. The 55-day activity was attributed to Cf^{254}, and the 2.2-year activity to Cf^{252}. Subsequently, it was shown that Cf^{254} always decays by spontaneous fission while Cf^{252} decays only 3 per cent of the time in this manner, decaying the re-mainder of the time by much lower-energy alpha decay. Simple analysis showed, then, that fifty times as much Cf^{252} relative to Cf^{254} was produced in the Eniwetok test, and one need only assume equal production of these isotopes in supernova events to obtain an energy input into supernova debris which would match the light output for at least 400 days. The Cf^{252} line in figure 15 would be dropped to the bottom of the figure.

Thus Burbidge, Burbidge, Christy, Fowler, and Hoyle originally and later in collaboration with Baade suggested that Cf^{254} is produced in type I supernovae and accounts for their unique light curves. In the hydrogen-bomb tests the Cf^{254} is produced by the radiation of the U^{238} incorporated in the

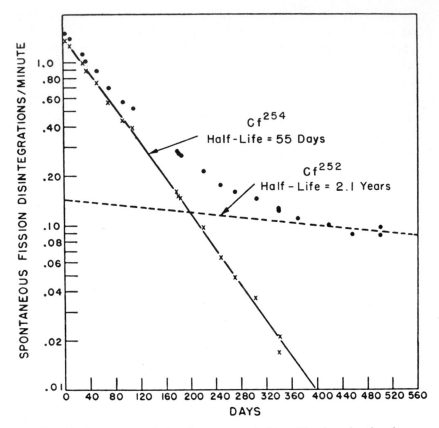

FIG. 15. Spontaneous fission decay curve of the californium fraction from thermonuclear debris. A decrease in relative intensity of the Cf^{252} activity to that of the Cf^{254} by a factor of the order of 50 is to be expected in a supernova explosion.

bomb by the intense flux of neutrons produced in the short interval of the explosion. Among many other events the U^{238} in some cases captured 16 neutrons to form U^{254}, and after the explosion the rapid beta-decay of this progenitor and its daughters eventually led to Cf^{254}. No intervening decays were fast enough to prevent the primary build-up of the U^{254}. Thus it was reasonable to assume in a supernova event that an even more intense neutron flux could produce Cf^{254} and other activities from the iron-group isotopes as "seed" nuclei. Among the nuclei produced in the supernova explosion are those which decay after the explosion to Th^{232}, U^{235} and U^{238}. The riddle of the origin of these nuclei is solved. The capture of neutrons in supernovae occurs at a *rapid* rate compared to beta-decay and alpha-decay near the valley of stability and it has consequently been termed the *r*-process. The path of the *r*-process is determined by equilibrium between the n,γ and γ,n processes; it must be remembered that the explosion generates a large gamma ray as well as neutron flux. For estimated temperatures of 10^9 degrees and neutron fluxes of 10^{34} per cm^2 per sec, the nuclei which are produced as often as they are lost in $n,\gamma \rightleftarrows \gamma,n$ have a neutron-binding energy of ~ 2 MeV. For a given A, these have a much higher neutron-proton ratio than the stable nuclei or those on the *s*-process path for which the neutron-binding energy is ~ 8 MeV. Progress along the *r* path occurs when one of these nuclei finally beta-decays, changing a neutron to a proton and permitting more neutrons to be added.

It will be noted that the *r* path bypasses natural alpha-particle radio-activity which stops the *s*-process and is, indeed, stopped only near $A = 275$ by neutron-induced fission. This fission cycles material back into the chain, and the nuclear species from $A \sim 115$ to 275 will grow in number as long as the neutron supply lasts, given only enough "seed" nuclei to start the process off. There is thus no difficulty in the *r*-process in producing the parents of the naturally radioactive series.

There are admittedly difficulties with the explanation of the light curves of type I supernovae. Cf^{254} is now known not to be unique among nuclear species in its mode of decay. There are indications that several other nuclei may have spontaneous fission lifetimes in the range from 10 to 100 days. Thus the light curves should not be unique and indeed they are not, but it is difficult to match the original correspondence between the decays of Cf^{254} and galaxy IC 4182. Numerous other suggestions have been made for the energy input in supernovae, one by the Burbidges and Hoyle and myself, and it will be some time before the entire truth will out concerning this puzzling problem.

However, it would be a shame to conclude without reference

66   NUCLEAR ASTROPHYSICS

to another "tale" involving supernova lore. Nothing can quite
hold a candle to the fascinating observations made by Chinese
astronomers on the supernova which occurred in 1054 exactly
in the sky where we now see the Crab nebula shown in the
frontispiece. These observations have been translated from the
ancient records by the Dutch classical scholar Duyvendak and
analyzed for astronomical content by the astronomers Mayall and
Oort. Table 5 sums it all up. What a remarkable coincidence
that the supernova first flared up on the Fourth of July, of all
days. (The dates have been corrected to the modern calendar.)
When they first saw it, the Chinese termed it a "guest star"
visible by day like Venus. What delicious terminology! This led
Mayall and Oort to an absolute-magnitude assignment of
−16.5 (see first of three points labeled Crab nebula in figure
13). The Chinese reported that they could see their guest
star in the daytime for 23 days until July 27, 1054. From the
daytime sensitivity of the eye, this gave −3.5 apparent magnitude and −15 absolute magnitude. Perhaps this was the cooling-
off period? Finally, the object disappeared even at night, after
627 more days, on April 17, 1056. The absolute magnitude
has been estimated as −5.5 from the nighttime sensitivity of
the eye, and thus there occurred a change of 9.5 magnitudes
over the 627 days. But 9.5 magnitudes is equivalent to 12
half-lives, and thus the half-life becomes 627/12, or 52 days,

TABLE 5

CHINESE OBSERVATIONS ON THE CRAB NEBULA*
(9.5 mag = 12 half-lives in 627 days. "Half-life" ≈ 52 days)

			App. mag.	Abs. mag
First observed	July 4, 1054	"Guest star visible by day like Venus"	-5	-16.5
Daylight visibility	July 27, 1054	23 days	-3.5	-15
Visible until	Apr. 17, 1056	650 days	6.0	- 5.5

* Duyvendak, *Publ. Astron. Soc. Pacific* **54** (1942): p. 91; Mayall and Oort,
ibid., p. 95.

FIG. 16. Petroglyph found on the wall of a cliff in Navajo Canyon in northern Arizona. The object below the crescent moon may well be the supernova observed by Chinese astronomers in 1054. There is substantial evidence that the Pueblo people inhabited the canyon at that time. (*Reproduced by courtesy of William C. Miller and the Museum of Northern Arizona.*)

very close to 55! Thus ancient Chinese astronomers measured the first radioactive half-life, that of Cf^{254}.

Californium 254! It is typical that California got into the act somehow. Much more justifiable is the case for Arizona. W. C. Miller of Mount Wilson and Palomar Observatories found the petroglyph illustrated in figure 16 on a cliff wall in Navajo Canyon in northern Arizona, which can reasonably be shown to have been occupied by Pueblo people in 1054. The petroglyph shows a crescent with a large circle below it in what may be taken as an attempt to depict a bright object just below the moon. At the suggestion of Hoyle, Miller referred to the chronological astronomical tables of Neugebauer[8] and found that early on the morning of July 5, 1054, before dawn, the crescent moon stood just 2° north of the supernova first reported by the Chinese the day before. May we not say that the Pueblo people share the discovery of the supernova with the Orientals!

Thus, we come to the end of the line in stellar nucleosynthesis. It goes without saying that there is considerably more work to do. To the experimentalist, this is an attractive feature of this point of view in that it leads to a program of cooperative research in the nuclear laboratory and in the astronomical observatory. Nuclear reactions can be studied by the nuclear physicist, and their effects in stars can be observed by the astrophysicist.

---

[8] P. V. Neugebauer, *Tafeln zur Astronomischen Chronologie* (1914) 2: "Tafeln der Sonne, Planeten und Mond."

III. *The Age of the Elements*

THE NATURAL HISTORY of the physical world in which we find ourselves is a subject of endless fascination to scientists and laymen alike. The simplest questions in this history involve *time*. When did it all begin? What is the age of the universe? Archbishop Ussher dated the *creation* in 4004 B.C. The astronomers of ancient India placed it much further back in time—several billion years ago. What do modern astronomical observations tell us?

When did our Galaxy, visible in part as the Milky Way, come into being? Look once more at the Virgo cluster of galaxies in figure 1 of Lecture I. When did the individual galaxies form in the cluster? All at the same time, or over a formation period of many billions of years? The Galaxy is a member of the local group or cluster of galaxies. Is it an old or a young cluster member? What is the age of the Galaxy?

When did the sun and the earth and the other planets take form in the Galaxy? Look once more at the Andromeda Nebula, our twin, in figure 2. Imagine that it is our Galaxy and that the sun is one of the bright spots of light in one of the spiral arms far from the central core. When did that spot light up? What is the age of the solar system?

When in this hierarchy of ages were nucleons created and the elements synthesized? What is the age of the elements? This is the principal question to which we seek some answer in this lecture, but, at the same time, we may be able to shed some light on the other questions which involve the temporal history of the astronomical systems of greatest interest to us.

THE AGE OF THE UNIVERSE

It has been pointed out many times that it is almost a matter of semantics to state that the age of the universe should

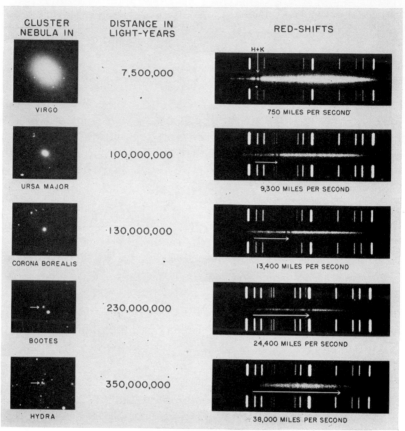

CLUSTER NEBULA IN	DISTANCE IN LIGHT-YEARS	RED-SHIFTS
VIRGO	7,500,000	750 MILES PER SECOND
URSA MAJOR	100,000,000	9,300 MILES PER SECOND
CORONA BOREALIS	130,000,000	13,400 MILES PER SECOND
BOOTES	230,000,000	24,400 MILES PER SECOND
HYDRA	350,000,000	38,000 MILES PER SECOND

FIG. 17. Relation between red shift and distance for extragalactic nebulae. Red shifts are expressed as velocities, $c\Delta\lambda/\lambda_0$. Arrows indicate shift for calcium lines H and K. One light year equals about 6 trillion miles, or 6×10^{12} miles. (*Mount Wilson and Palomar Observatories.*)

be greater than, or equal to, the age of the Galaxy and that, in turn, the age of the Galaxy should be greater than, or equal to, that of the stellar systems it contains, including the solar system. In the latter case it is tacitly assumed that stellar systems condensed from the gaseous state in the Galaxy and were not captured ready-formed by the Galaxy.

The age of the universe is derived from observations of the red shift of light from distant galaxies. This was discussed briefly in Lecture I but here we must look somewhat more carefully at what is involved in the nature and interpretation

of these observations. To do this let us consider figure 17. At
the top right of this figure we see the spectrum of the light
received from an elliptical galaxy (or nebula) in the Virgo
cluster of galaxies. Spectra from galaxies in other clusters are
shown below in the remainder of the figure. The Virgo spectrum was obtained by letting the light entering the telescope
from the galaxy fall on a diffraction grating. The grating
reflects light of different wave length or color at different
angles and thus the reflected light can be made to fall in
different locations on a recording photographic plate. In figure
17 the redder the light, the farther to the right it falls; the
bluer the light, the farther to the left. Light from a standard,
laboratory source containing bright, emission lines of known
wave length is also reflected by the grating but in such a way
as to fall above and below the nebular spectrum. In this way
the wave length or color scale of the spectrum is calibrated.
The Virgo spectrum is seen to consist of a continuum of "white"
light broken by two closely spaced, dark lines which are known
as the H and K lines of the element calcium. The wave
lengths of these lines are known from laboratory measurements
to be characteristic of the calcium atom. The lines occur
because calcium atoms in the atmospheres of the stars in the
elliptical galaxy absorb light of this wave length and thus
produce a gap in the emission continuum. In the light from
the galaxy in Virgo the H and K lines appear only slightly to
the red side of where they are expected from laboratory observations. But it will be noted in the succeeding spectra, below
the top one, that the two lines are shifted more and more to
the right, that is, the lines exhibit greater and greater red
shifts.

Figure 17 has been prepared to illustrate the important
feature of the red shift observations which was discovered by
Edwin Hubble. It will be noted that the size of the images
of the elliptical galaxies chosen from the Virgo, Ursa Major,
Corona Borealis, Bootes and Hydra clusters decrease from top
to bottom, that is, as the red shift increases. It is assumed that
all these galaxies have the same actual size and that the apparent size is a distance indicator—the more distant the galaxy

the smaller the image. In practice the information obtained
from the images on the photographic plates is translated into
apparent luminosity. In general the smaller the image the
smaller the apparent luminosity. It is assumed that this latter
quantity varies as the inverse square of the distance to the
galaxy. Thus if one galaxy has one-fourth the apparent luminosity of another galaxy, assumed to have the same absolute
luminosity, then it is twice as far away as this other galaxy.

Hubble assumed that the red shift is a Doppler effect arising
from recessional motion. If the galaxies are moving away
from us, the time between the arrival of successive light pulses
will be greater than the time interval between emission of the
pulses because of the distance moved by the galaxy during this
interval. Thus the frequency of the arriving light is lowered or
the wave length is lengthened—this last, because the wave length
is equal to the velocity of light *divided* by the frequency. Furthermore, the greater the velocity of the emitting galaxy the
greater is the red shift expected to be. Thus the correlation of
increasing red shift with decreasing apparent size or luminosity
in figure 17 is interpreted to mean that the more distant
galaxies are moving with the greater velocity. In fact, the
observations indicate a linear relation between red shift or
velocity and the luminosity-distance, as it is properly called.
The constant of proportionality has been called Hubble's
constant.

The simplest explanation of this relationship is that of an
expanding universe in which all of the matter was at one
time ejected with a spread of velocities from a common region;
the galaxies whose matter received the greatest velocities relative to that of our own are now the most distant from us. Note
that this will be the conclusion of observers in other galaxies,
too. The general expansion means that all galaxies are in
relative recessional motion. As long as the region of observation is limited and the "edge" of the universe cannot be observed, no center of the expansion can be established. We are
not in a *preferred* position just because we see galaxies in
recession in all directions.

If you question this, consider two galaxies along the same

line of sight, the second one twice as far away as the first. Then by Hubble's law the second one is moving twice as fast as the first relative to us. Now, consider yourself as an observer on the first galaxy, which is halfway between us and the second. As you look back at the rest of us you will see the Milky Way receding with the same speed that you originally ascribed to the first galaxy you are now on. Furthermore, as you turn around and look at the second galaxy, it will be receding with this same speed since the second galaxy has the same speed *relative* to the first as the *first* has to the Milky Way. Thus you still see a general expansion and if you consider a few more galaxies, even along different lines of sight, you will soon convince yourself that a linear velocity-distance relation observed from one galaxy is a linear relation observed from another. It is the only relation which works in this manner for nearby galaxies. For distant observers the relation becomes more complicated but remains the same for all observers.

Quantitatively, the velocity is equal to the velocity of light multiplied by the fractional red shift, that is, the observed shift in wave length divided by the laboratory wave length. This holds as long as the fraction is not more than a few tenths. Thus if the distance can be established on an absolute scale and if it is divided by the velocity, then the time back to the origin of the expansion—the age of the universe, no less—can be calculated. This is just the reciprocal of Hubble's constant and in round numbers according to current observations is about 10 billion years.

It will be clear from the preceding paragraphs that there are many "ifs" in the interpretation of the red shift measurements. In plain words, there are numerous reasons for uncertainty as to the age of the universe. Hubble's original value, *circa* 1930, was 2 billion years. The major difficulty lies in the determination of the distance scale. This obviously cannot be done directly with measuring rods nor by bouncing radio or light signals off galaxies as we do off the moon in order to determine its distance. The method used is indirect, involving the empirical relation between the period and absolute

luminosity of certain variable stars called cepheids. The distance to certain nearby cepheids in our Galaxy can be measured
by so-called parallax observations using the known diameter
of the earth's orbit around the sun as a base line. The apparent luminosity of these cepheids can then be translated
into absolute luminosity. The period of the variability is
found to be correlated with this absolute luminosity. Thus
when the period of a cepheid in a nearby galaxy is measured,
its absolute luminosity can be calculated and from its observed
apparent luminosity the distance to the cepheid and thus to
the galaxy can be determined. Even this indirect method can
only be used for nearby galaxies—cepheids cannot be resolved
in faint, distant galaxies. Thus the luminosity-distance technique must be employed in these latter cases.

By the year 1952, Walter Baade had definitely established
the need for revision in the zero-point of the period-absolute
luminosity relation for the cepheids. Since Baade's work
showed that the relevant cepheids were intrinsically brighter
than previously thought, the result was an expansion of the
distance scale, a decrease in Hubble's constant and an increase
in its reciprocal to approximately 5 billion years. This change
from 2 to 5 billion years is typical of the revisions which have
resulted in the increase to the presently accepted value of about
10 billion years.

There are other more fundamental difficulties and in my first
lecture I promised to discuss these in this lecture. According to
Einstein's theory of relativity, the dependence of the red shift
on velocity is much more complicated than the linear dependence which holds for low values of these two variables.
Our ordinary experience gives us no check on this complexity.
When light is shifted redward its energy content is decreased
and the apparent luminosity is changed by this effect as well
as by the inverse square of the distance. Unfortunately the
correction to be made for this effect is dependent on the past
history of the universe and not just on what can be observed,
nearby, now.

Equating the age of the universe to the reciprocal of the
Hubble constant, as was done above, assumes that the velocity

has been constant since the original big bang. This has not necessarily been the case and different models of the universe yield different variations of the velocity with time depending on the accelerations or decelerations implicit in the models. If the velocities were greater in the past, then the age of the universe is less than 10 billion years; if the velocities were less in the past, then the age of the universe is greater than 10 billion years. Allowing for all these theoretical complexities and observational uncertainties, the age of the universe on the evolutionary, expanding models, cannot be specified exactly but probably falls in the range from 7 to 15 billion years. On the steady state model in which the expansion is compensated for by the steady creation of matter and the formation of new galaxies the age is, of course, infinite. Finally it must be emphasized that what are observed are red shifts and luminosities. We interpret these observations in terms of velocities, accelerations, distances, and ages in terms of our ordinary experience. Einstein's general theory of relativity relates the red shifts and luminosities in very general ways which do not necessarily require these interpretations. Thus we must proceed with the greatest care in speaking of the age of the universe until we know more about the observations, which are probing what seem to be the depths of space, and, in terms of our ordinary ideas of light travel time, events which occurred in the very distant past. For the moment we must accept even the range from 7 to 15 billion years as the age of the universe with considerable reservation.

THE AGE OF THE GALAXY

In Lecture I it was noted that "fifteen billion years ago our Galaxy was not at all like it is at the present time." At that time stars began to form in what had previously been a rotating, roughly spherical mass of primordial gas. With the formation of stars one speaks of the "birth" of the Galaxy. The question remains—how it is known that the birth date was "fifteen billion years ago." To answer this question it is necessary to digress for a moment to certain relevant considerations concerning astronomical observations.

Astronomical observations yield two basic data about a star, its magnitude and its color. The absolute magnitude of a star is related to its luminosity L in ergs per second through the relation

Absolute magnitude $= 88.6 - \log_{2.5} L = 88.6 - 2.5 \log_{10} L$.

The sun, with an output of 3.8×10^{33} ergs/sec, has an absolute magnitude of 4.6. Thus in terms of the solar luminosity, $L_\odot$, one has

$$\text{Absolute magnitude} = 4.6 - 2.5 \log_{10} L/L_\odot.$$

For example a star 10^4 times as bright as the sun has absolute magnitude equal to -5.4. Note that magnitude is a logarithmic quantity and that small or negative magnitudes mean large luminosity. First magnitude stars are brighter than second magnitude stars and so on. The equations given above have been adopted since the visual magnitude scale used by early astronomers is equivalent to a factor of 10 in luminosity for each 2.5 magnitudes.

In addition, note that it is not easy to determine the absolute magnitude of a star, since this requires the establishment of its distance from the earth. The color of a star is an indication of its surface temperature, red stars having temperatures around 3000° absolute and blue stars running as high as ten times this value. When magnitude is plotted versus decreasing surface temperature (blue stars to the left, red to the right) in a so-called Hertzsprung-Russell, or HR diagram, all stars of homogeneous composition fall roughly on a smooth curve and are termed main-sequence stars. The location of this curve is indicated in figure 18, which we shall return to later. Massive stars, with, say, 10 times a solar mass, develop high internal temperatures and densities which in turn lead to rapid nuclear reaction rates, large energy generation, and high luminosity. Radiation of the great energy generated requires high surface temperatures, and so massive stars are blue in color as well as very luminous up to 10^4 times as bright as the sun. The sun is yellow in color and of about average luminosity as main-sequence stars go. Stars less massive than the sun, say 0.1

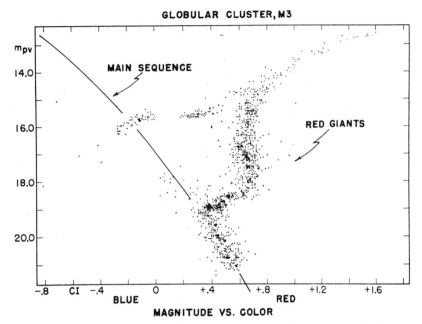

FIG. 18. The Hertzsprung-Russell or magnitude-color diagram for individual stars of the globular cluster M3 found by Sandage and his collaborators using the 200-inch Hale telescope on Mount Palomar and the 100 inch Hooker telescope on Mount Wilson. The locus for main-sequence stars is also shown for comparison. Stars off the main sequence have evolved through exhaustion of their central hydrogen fuel.

times a solar mass, are red in color and have luminosities about 1 per cent of that of the sun. A *mass-luminosity* law has been established by astronomers from which a star's mass can be estimated if its absolute luminosity can be determined. Now the lifetime of a star, as determined by the amount of its nuclear fuel, will be roughly proportional to its mass divided by its luminosity. It is estimated that the sun will have existed for 10 billion years in round numbers before it exhausts its central hydrogen. Stars of 10 times a solar mass, burning 10^4 times as brightly, have lifetimes of only 10 million years, while those of 0.1 times a solar mass with only 1 per cent solar luminosity will live 100 billion years. To recapitulate, then, massive, short-lived, bright blue stars lie on the upper left-hand portion of the main-sequence curve, while stars less massive than the sun, long-lived, dull, and red, lie on the lower right-hand portion. Where a star lies on the curve depends essentially upon the mass of the gas which gravitationally contracted to form the star.

I have previously discussed the burning of hydrogen during a star's main-sequence stage and the evolution into red giants as the hydrogen becomes exhausted in the central regions of the star. Evidence for the evolution of stars from their main-sequence stage into their red-giant stage as their composition changes is found most conclusively in magnitude-color studies of globular clusters. A typical globular cluster lying in the halo of the Galaxy is illustrated in figure 19, and the magnitude-color diagram found by Sandage for the globular cluster designated as M3 is shown in figure 18. Globular clusters are groups of the order of 10^5 stars which formed in a localized spherical region in the Galaxy. It is assumed that these stars all formed at much the same time, so that they are all of the same age. In figure 18 each point represents the laborious

Fig. 19. The globular cluster of stars in *Canes Venatici*. (*Mount Wilson and Palomar Observatories*.)

determination of both the magnitude and color of an individual star in the cluster using the 200-inch Hale telescope on Mount Palomar. There is one great simplification in that the correction from apparent magnitude to absolute magnitude is the same for all members of the cluster. In figure 18, we note that the upper part of the main sequence is missing; the short-lived, massive stars have long since evolved and in their later stages slowly or explosively ejected their mass into the region between the stars where it is not visible.

Stars which have just exhausted their central hydrogen in M3 now lie at the left on the lower horizontal, giant branch in figure 18. Since the distance to M3 can be determined from the apparent luminosity and periods of its variable stars, it is possible to estimate the absolute luminosity and then the mass of the stars which have just left the main sequence. Now all we need to know is what fraction of the star must be completely depleted in hydrogen when the star leaves the main sequence in order to calculate its lifetime on the main sequence. Since star formation times are relatively short this main-sequence lifetime is approximately the star's age and since all the stars are assumed to have formed at the same time, this is then the age of the globular cluster. Age is betrayed by outward appearances in humans and stars alike. In the case of stars the give-away comes in the first blush of red-gianthood.

It is possible to estimate theoretically the mass of the hydrogen-depleted core which leads to the red-giant stage. This mass is roughly 12 to 20 per cent of the total mass depending on the composition and other properties of the star. In this uncertainty lies the rub but let us take 16 per cent as a good average for the moment.

The argument goes like this. Let us assume constant luminosity in the main sequence and no great change on first leaving the main sequence. Designate this luminosity in ergs per year by the letter L. Before finishing our calculation it will prove convenient to measure L relative to the luminosity of the sun, $L_\odot$, which is equal to 3.8×10^{33} ergs per second or 1.2×10^{41} ergs per year. The lifetime on the main sequence is given by the energy available divided by the luminosity. The more fuel available the longer the stellar fires will burn; the greater the luminosity, the faster the energy store is expended. Now the energy available is the number of ergs released per gram of hydrogen transformed into helium times the fuel available which is just 16 per cent of the total mass according to the previous discussion. Designate the mass in grams by the letter M. For comparison the mass of the sun, $M_\odot$, is equal to 2×10^{33} grams. It is now possible to calculate the lifetime, call it τ in years, for any mass M and any main-sequence luminosity L if it is recalled from Lecture I that the energy release in hydrogen burning is 6.4×10^{18} ergs per gram. The lifetime is

$$\tau = \frac{0.16 \times 6.4 \times 10^{18} \times 2 \times 10^{33} \; (M/M_\odot)}{1.2 \times 10^{41} \; (L/L_\odot)} \text{ years}$$

$$= 17 \times 10^9 \frac{M/M_\odot}{L/L_\odot} \text{ years}$$

$$= 17 \frac{M/M_\odot}{L/L_\odot} \text{ billion years.}$$

Note that the mass and luminosity of the star have been expressed relative to the mass and luminosity of the sun, respectively, by multiplying and dividing through by these latter quantities. The equation as stated yields 17 billion years for the main-sequence lifetime of the sun. However, it is believed that the sun originally contained only 71 per cent hydrogen by mass, the remainder being mostly helium with a few per cent heavier elements. This means that it will require 71 per cent of the time calculated above for the hydrogen in the sun's burning region to be depleted and the predicted lifetime becomes approximately 12 billion years. This is a better approximation than the round number of 10 billion years used in some of the previous discussion. When the sun does become a red giant, with an envelope of hot, reducing gas expanding throughout the planetary system, the earth will hardly be inhabitable to say the least. It is comforting to

THE AGE OF THE ELEMENTS

know that this holocaust is 12–4.8 = 7.2 billion years away.[1] It would be still more comforting if we could be so sanguine about potential holocausts of our own making.

Return now to M3 which was chosen for discussion because it is representative of globular clusters which have stars with nearly the lowest measured luminosities which have already moved off the main sequence. These low luminosities are very close to that of the sun but remember that, in M3, stars with this luminosity have already entered the giant stage. Refer to figure 18 again. The use of the lifetime equation given above results in the value 17 billion years if M3 originally was formed from practically pure hydrogen and 12 billion years if the primordial material contained only 71 per cent hydrogen. Thus the problem which has plagued us constantly throughout these lectures—what was the primordial helium content in the oldest stellar systems which formed in the Galaxy—raises its head again. Did a big bang beginning produce helium before the Galaxy formed or did supermassive stars form first in the Galaxy and, in evolving and returning material to the interstellar medium, produce helium in significant amount before the oldest stars we can now observe were formed? At this time we just do not know and thus we must accept the uncertainty of several billion years in the age of the Galaxy's oldest stars and thus in the age to be assigned to the Galaxy itself.

The discussion just presented has emphasized only one of the numerous uncertainties—that of initial composition—which besets age determinations. The full range of M3 ages which are presently bandied about by the experts extends from 10 to 20 billion years. This range is to be compared with that for the age of the universe in the evolutionary cosmologies, which was found to be 7 to 15 billion years in the first part of this lecture.

The uncertainty in the two ages is exasperating for some, comforting for others. The evolutionary cosmologists argue that the uncertainties still permit the universe to be older than the Galaxy. (They are required to form the Galaxy fairly

---

[1] The value of 4.8 billion years for the present age of the sun will be discussed in more detail in what follows.

early in any case.) The steady state cosmologists with their
infinite age for the universe wish the numbers could be tied
down so as to show a definite inconsistency in their rivals'
philosophy—the Galaxy older than the universe. For the rest
of us, the most interesting point may well be that the solar
system has an age considerably less than these just found for
the grand-scale systems of our environment. It is time we
turned to a closer look at the details in the determination of
the age of the "local" scene, the solar system.

THE AGE OF THE SOLAR SYSTEM

Radioactive clocks are the key to the techniques used by
nuclear geophysicists to measure the age of objects in the solar
system and thus to infer the age of the system itself. First
let us discuss these solar system objects—rocks and meteorites.

The dating of the rocks chronicles the history of formation
of the earth's crust and, fascinating as this history is, it reaches
back only some 3 billion years or so and I shall not dwell upon
it, for the meteorites reveal even a greater age, 4.5 to 5 billion
years. Meteorites are chunks of stone and metal which are
intercepted by the earth in its motion through the solar system
and are, in particular, those chunks which successfully penetrate the earth's atmosphere and reach the earth's surface. The
smaller more fragile objects make meteor trails but it is the
meteorites which survive the last crucial moments of their free
flight to become objects of curiosity in terrestrial museums
and laboratories.

The origin of the meteorites is obscure except in one detail
—the available information on the trajectory of their passage
through the atmosphere, when observed, indicates that these
bodies originate somewhere in the solar system. Some astronomers argue that the meteorites came from the asteroid belt
which falls mainly between Mars and Jupiter; others argue
that some meteorites at least have been knocked off the moon
either by other meteorites or by comets. For our purposes it
is sufficient that the meteorites represent solar system material.

Let us adopt the asteroid belt hypothesis and the following
general view of the history of the solar system. The planets

formed within a few tens or hundreds of millions of years of the formation of the sun. Something went wrong in the asteroid belt and the formation of one or more lunar or planet size bodies in this region was followed by disruption, perhaps through collisions, into the asteroidal bodies which range from one to several hundred kilometers in diameter. Relatively recent collisions between asteroids send meteorite chunks out of the belt into trajectories which eventually intercept that of the earth.

These details of meteorite history may be all fancy but there does seem to be one common point of agreement. The meteorites and the parent bodies in which they were formed had a complicated but relatively short early history at the beginning of the solar system. Since that time the meteorites have remained substantially unchanged in chemical and physical structure. Allowances must be made for the recent collision at relatively low velocity in the asteroid belt, for bombardment by the cosmic radiation, for loss of the noble, rare gases by diffusion, for ablation of outer material on penetration through the earth's atmosphere and for the shock of collision with the earth—but these allowances can be made through keen and patient analysis.

Thus for the greater part of their life span the meteorites are cold, inert bodies with only one important set of physical processes taking place—the inexorable transformations of natural radioactivity which I briefly touched upon in Lecture I. Here I must repeat and elaborate. Th^{232}, U^{235} and U^{238} decay with half-lives of 13.9, 0.70, and 4.5 billion years through a complicated set of alpha-particle (He^4) and beta-ray ($e^- \bar{\nu}$) emissions to three stable isotopes of lead, Pb^{208}, Pb^{207}, and Pb^{206}, respectively.

One can refer to these radioactive nuclei as radioactive clocks or chronometers but a more accurate analogy is the *hourglass* and perhaps the most apt description is *aeonglass*. The sand in the upper part of the hourglass in figure 20 represents the still untransformed parent nuclei, for example, U^{238}. The sand in the lower part represents the final, stable decay product or daughter, for example Pb^{206}. Now the amount of

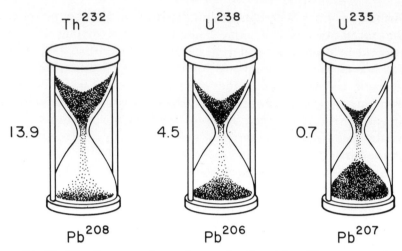

FIG. 20. The three *aeonglasses* of natural radioactivity. The parent activity is indicated above the neck of the aeonglass, the eventual stable daughter product below. The half lives are indicated in billions of years.

U^{238} and Pb^{206} in a given meteorite sample can in principle be determined. Similarly the hourglass can in principle be graduated to yield the relative amounts of sand in the upper and lower portions at the *beginning* and *end* of a given time interval and thus an interval up to one hour in duration can be measured with the hourglass or up to one day with a *dayglass* and so on.

The catch in all this will now be apparent. Geophysicists can make measurements on the relative amounts of parent and daughter nuclei only *now,* at the end of the time interval they are attempting to measure. There is abundant evidence that the meteorites contained primordial lead as well as uranium and thorium at the time that their composition became fixed and that the relative primordial element abundances varied from meteorite sample to meteorite sample.

But the geophysicists have not been stymied by this difficulty. In some cases the helium resulting from the decay can be measured and it frequently is reasonable to assume that the original helium content was negligible and that radiogenic helium was not lost in the life span of the meteorite. These assumptions pose big ifs. There are other tricks of the trade but the most accurate results came from the so-called lead-lead method used by my colleague Claire Patterson. This uses the aeonglasses in *pairs*, particularly the U^{235}-U^{238} pair, in observations on a number of meteorites and takes advantage of the fact that the relative abundances of the inseparable uranium isotopes, U^{235} and U^{238}, were originally the same in all meteorites and similarly for the relative abundances of the inseparable lead isotopes, Pb^{207} and Pb^{206}, even though the U/Pb ratio was clearly variable then and now from meteorite to meteorite. As a matter of fact all that need be measured are the isotopic ratios U^{235}/U^{238} and Pb^{207}/Pb^{206} *now* in a number of meteorites. Then the relative amount of Pb^{207} is plotted against the relative amount of Pb^{206}. If all the meteorites have the same age such a plot is a straight line called an isochron and this is what is observed. Meteorites with relatively large amounts of uranium originally have relatively larger amounts of lead now. The slope of this line depends on the known decay lifetimes and increases with the age of the meteorites which can thus be determined. It is mathematically important that the radioactive decay is exponential—a fixed fraction per unit time—and not linear with time as in the case of the conventional hourglass. The important point is that the Pb^{207}/U^{235} ratio increases more rapidly with time than the Pb^{206}/U^{238} ratio since the U^{235} lifetime is shorter than that of U^{238}. Thus the slope of long-time isochrons is greater than that of short-time isochrons. The isochron that fits Patterson's measurements corresponds to a meteorite age between 4.5 and 4.6 billion years. Allowing for a few hundred million years for the formation of the meteorite parent bodies leads to the frequently quoted value of 4.8 billion years for the age of the solar system but the uncertainty is such that a more correct statement is that the age probably falls in the range from 4.5 to 5.0 billion years. There can be little doubt however, as I have emphasized before, that the solar system is much younger than the Galaxy, in round numbers by some 10 billion years.

There is one independent check on the age of the solar system determined by radioactivity in meteorites. Detailed theoretical studies of the structure of the sun, using its known

mass and reasonable assumptions about its composition, indicate that it has taken the sun about 5 billion years to attain
its presently observed radius and luminosity. This relatively
great age is only possible on the basis that nuclear reactions
are the source of the sun's energy. Before this was realized,
gravitational contraction seemed the only source of energy.
Lord Kelvin showed that this hypothesis, due to Helmholtz,
necessarily dates the birth of the sun about 20 million years
ago. When the study of the radioactivity in rocks led to much
greater ages for the earth, Eddington gleefully remarked:

> Lord Kelvin's date of the creation of the sun is treated
> with no more respect than Archbishop Ussher's.

Nucleocosmochronology

Every scientist likes to invent long words and I use *nucleo-
cosmochronology* to describe the dating of nucleosynthesis or
the determination of the age of the elements. The dating
method was first suggested by the Burbidges and Hoyle and me
and uses the uranium-theorium decays just as in geochronology.
The most recent computations have been made by two gradu-
ates of our laboratory, Donald Clayton and Philip Seeger, in
collaboration with me. In fact Clayton has invented a new
method using the radioactive decay of rhenium, Rh^{187}, to
osmium, Os^{187}.

In order to measure the time and duration of nucleosynthesis
it is necessary to stipulate the relative amounts of Th^{232}, U^{235}
and U^{238} formed in this synthesis. In Lecture II the production of these nuclei in the r process in supernovae has already
been discussed. The detailed study of this process indicates
that Th^{232} and U^{235} are produced 50 to 80 per cent more
abundantly than U^{238} largely because they have a greater
number of short-lived radioactive parents than does U^{238}. These
progenitors are also produced in supernova explosions and
rapidly add to the abundance of the three long-lived nuclei.
The analysis is usually done with the ratios Th^{232}/U^{238} and
U^{235}/U^{238}, that is, all three aeonglasses are used but only the
ratios involving the upper portions of these glasses are employed.

The ratios at the origin of the solar system are calculated from the present ratios in meteorites, the known decay times and the age of the solar system as determined by the methods previously described. At the origin of the solar system one thus finds $Th^{232}/U^{238} = 2.3$ and $U^{235}/U^{238} = 0.40$. Note that Th^{232}/U^{238} decreases as we go back in time since Th^{232} has a longer life-time than U^{238} while U^{235}/U^{238} increases as we go back in time. Thus we must extrapolate back in time before the origin of the solar system until these ratios fall in the range 1.5 to 1.8 as indicated by the r process calculations. How this extrapolation is made depends upon the model of nucleosynthesis assumed. One model assumes a single r process event, the original "big bang" or a super-supernova. The extrapolation of the two ratios on this model does not lead to concordant results for the date of the single event. Better results are obtained on the basis of a long period of r process nucleosynthesis in many supernovae with contributions terminating, in so far as solar system material is concerned, when the sun's proto-cloud contracted and no longer mixed with the remainder of the galactic gases. On this model of continuous synthesis in the Galaxy the duration is found to be 5 to 10 billion years. Thus there is no single age for the elements. The nuclear material of the solar system was produced over a period comparable in length to the lifetime of the Galaxy before the origin of the solar system. The simplest hypothesis is that new element contributions to the galactic gas started with the terminal explosions of the first stars in the Galaxy and continues up to the present time. Solar system abundances became fixed except for radioactivity and cosmic ray effects 4.8 billion years ago.

SUMMARY

It is well to recapitulate the long history of astronomical systems and nuclear processes in them in spite of all the uncertainities in our observations and understanding. On the steady state cosmology the universe is infinitely old; on the evolutionary cosmologies the age of the universe falls in the range from 7 to 15 billion years. The exhaustion of nuclear fuel in globular clusters of stars reveals the age of the Galaxy to be from 10 to 20 billion years with 15 billion the most probable value. There is no certain conflict in the universal and galactic ages in the evolutionary cosmologies. The elements have probably been produced in stars over the full history of the Galaxy. The sun is a late newcomer on the scene—the solar system is only 4.5 to 5.0 billion years old. Never mind, the sun will exceed 12 billion years in age before it encompasses the planets in its fiery embrace as a red giant. There is great comfort in youth no matter on what time scale.

This summary is presented in spite of all the uncertainties but not without concluding with the wise words of Samuel Pepys:

> To the Rhenish wine-house, and there came Jonas Moore, the mathematician, to us . . . and spoke very many things not so much to prove the Scripture false, as that the time therein is not well computed nor understood.—Diary of Samuel Pepys, 23 May, 1661.

Three hundred years later it is perhaps well to admit the possibility that the time *herein* is not well computed nor understood.

IV. Supermassive Stars, Quasars, Extragalactic Radio Sources, and Galactic Explosions[1]

D URING THE PAST TWO DECADES a revolution has occurred in astronomy and astrophysics. The heroes of this revolution are the radio astronomers who have not only detected radio waves from extragalactic sources but have devised techniques for pin-pointing the location of these sources on the celestial sphere. In the forefront of these efforts have been radio astronomers throughout the world—in Australia, England, the Netherlands, the Soviet Union, and the United States.

In this lecture, I wish to discuss first of all the observational work which makes possible the identification of radio sources with optical objects observable through large telescopes. Secondly, I wish to discuss the suggestions which Fred Hoyle, Geoffrey Burbidge, Margaret Burbidge, and I have made concerning the source of the prodigious energies involved in the radio objects. Our primary concern has been just this—what physical phenomenon is the source of the energy? Ordinary stars shine on nuclear energy. Are the nuclear resources in supermassive stars sufficient to meet the observed energy requirements in radio objects or must we turn to other mechanisms—gravitation, stellar collisions, or what you will, to explain radio "galaxies" and "stars"? In case nuclear reactions in supermassive stars are effective, then we must ask whether these stars are stable or unstable during nuclear burning. In addition, the mechanisms of transfer of energy from the form in which it is produced to the exotic forms exhibited in the radio sources must be given some attention.

[1] This lecture is a revised and updated version of a paper originally presented before the American Philosophical Society in Philadelphia on April 24, 1964, and published in the *Proceedings* of the Society, vol. **109**, 3 (1965): p. 181.

The Optical Identification of Radio Sources

The break-through in the observation and identification of radio sources has been made possible by the development and construction in several locations throughout the world of radio telescopes capable of making position determinations to better than ten seconds in angle. As one example, radio astronomers of the California Institute of Technology, using funds furnished by the Office of Naval Research, have constructed at the Owens Valley Radio Observatory in Bishop, California, an interferometer consisting of two 90-foot dishes (fig. 21) which can be separated on railroad tracks up to distances of 1,000 meters. Since the radio waves studied are of the order of 30 centimeters in wave length, each dish is capable of an angular resolution near one part in one thousand, while the interferometer arrangement yields a limiting resolution near one part in ten thousand. Under construction are additional dishes, funded by the National Science Foundation, which will yield even higher resolution.

The precise determination of the position of a radio object makes possible an accurate comparison with the position of optical objects visible through large conventional telescopes which have very high angular resolution because of the short wave length of visible light. The ultimate objective is to make an *identification* of the radio source with an optical object. Radio astronomers at the California Institute of Technology have the unique advantage of being able to cooperate with staff members of the Mount Wilson and Palomar Observatories in using the 200-inch Hale telescope on Mount Palomar for making position comparisons and identifications.

Early identifications, made before great precision had been reached in the radio observations, indicated that in some cases radio sources seemed to be associated with pairs of galaxies in close proximity and perhaps even in collision. This led naturally to the assumption that the energy freed in such a collision might be the source of the radio energy. It is now believed that collision energy is inadequate in this regard but, more importantly, the great majority of the more precise identifications for radio sources outside of our Galaxy, the

FIG. 21. The 90-foot dishes of the Owens Valley Radio Observatory near Bishop, California. The dishes can be moved on over-size railway tracks so that they can be used as radio interferometers at separations up to 3,000 feet. (*J. R. Eyerman.*)

Milky Way, are with single, isolated galaxies and not with pairs of galaxies.

As a matter of fact the high angular resolution of present-day radio observations makes possible not only unambiguous optical identifications but also yields a detailed picture of the intensity contours or "structure" of the radio source. Many of the radio sources consist primarily of two widely separated components with a single galaxy located quite precisely on the line of centers of the two components and in some cases approximately at the centroid calculated from the relative strengths of the two components. For example, the radio source in the constellation Centaurus consists principally of two roughly equal components extending over a region of at least 4° by 10° in extent and with a separation of the most intense regions of the two components equal to approximately 2.5°. Very close to the middle and on the line of centers lies the galaxy NGC 5128 (also called Centaurus A) which exhibits a dark equatorial dust lane and a

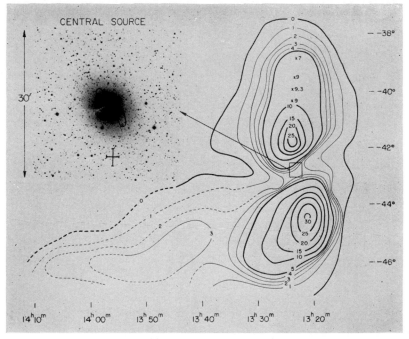

FIG. 22. The extended, extragalactic radio source in the constellation *Centaurus*. The source consists primarily of the two components indicated by the radio emission contours. Along the line of centers of the two components lies the galaxy NGC 5128, also called *Centaurus A,* which is shown in the inset (negative print) and in more detail in figure 23 (positive print). The ovals in the inset represent the general outlines of a second pair of radio-emitting regions associated with NGC 5128.

FIG. 23. The almost spherical galaxy, NGC 5128 or *Centaurus A*, showing the band of obscuring gas and dust which encircles it. This galaxy lies at the center of the powerful radio source shown in figure 22. (*Mount Wilson and Palomar Observatories.*)

spherical halo of stars with diameter of the order of 10 seconds of arc. The radio source and the galaxy are illustrated in figures 22 and 23.

Thus, NGC 5128 is dwarfed by the optically invisible radio source associated with it. Nonetheless, the *association* is so convincing that it is generally agreed that the invisible particles and fields in the two radio components must have been ejected from the galaxy in opposite directions in some distant time in the past. Since the separation is the order of 10^6 light years in magnitude, the ejection must have occurred at least 10^6 years ago. Even more detailed studies of the radio emission indicate two additional but weaker and smaller components very close to NGC 5128, in fact, not much more than 10^4 light years from the center. Whatever this galaxy has done, it has done it twice!

ENERGY REQUIREMENTS OF THE RADIO SOURCES

The separation distances just quoted illustrate the important quantitative aspect of the identification of radio sources with optical galaxies. Since it is the angular separation which is measured, the calculation of the linear separation requires a knowledge of the distance to the source. Until recently there has been no way to determine directly the distance to the radio objects of interest, although red shift measurements have been made on the 21-cm atomic hydrogen line from nearby objects and are being rapidly extended to more distant objects. On the other hand the distance to the galaxy can be calculated if optical red shift measurements have been made and if the red shift is assumed to be proportional to distance in accordance with Hubble's Law as discussed in Lecture III.

It is, of course, possible to question the validity of Hubble's Law, and the conclusions which follow upon its acceptance might be taken to be such that abandonment of the law may ultimately be necessary. However, in the optical red shift measurements on *galaxies* to date, there is no indication of a significant departure from linearity in the relation between red shift and *luminosity distance* even to the point where the shifted wave lengths are almost fifty per cent greater than the laboratory values. Regardless of the ultimate significance of the luminosity distance, it is this distance which is used in the inverse square law to derive absolute luminosity or magnitude from the measured apparent values. In essence the red shift is used to translate the apparent optical luminosity of a galaxy into the absolute value and it is a natural and simple extension to make the identical translation for the radio luminosity of the associated radio source. This procedure has received strong support quite recently from the work of Allen Sandage, who has shown that the galaxies associated with extended radio sources exhibit the same optical red shift relation as the brightest members of galactic clusters. For other reasons radio galaxies are thought to be among the most luminous and most massive galaxies known.

Identification with an optically red-shifted galaxy thus makes it possible to determine the absolute luminosity of radio sources from the measured apparent luminosity, that is, the radio flux at the earth in erg cm^{-2} sec $^{-1}$ can be translated into the total rate of energy emission in erg sec^{-1} at the source with the additional assumption of isotropic emission. (The possibility that the radio waves are directed at the earth is rightly given scant attention.) The results are staggering. More than 50 radio sources have been listed by Thomas A. Matthews, William W. Morgan, and Maarten Schmidt with luminosities exceeding 10^{38} erg sec^{-1} and ranging up to 2×10^{45} erg sec $^{-1}$, the value for 3C 295 (the 295th object in the third Cambridge University catalogue of radio sources). The optical luminosity of the sun is 4×10^{33} erg sec^{-1} and that from our Galaxy is approximately 10^{43} erg sec^{-1}. Thus 3C 295 has a radio luminosity almost one million million times that of the optical emission from the sun and more than 100 times that from our Galaxy.

The total amounts of energy required to sustain these luminosities can be calculated in several ways. It is reasonable to assume that the minimum age to be assigned to the sources is that given by dividing the observed dimensions by the velocity of light. Actually the linear growth of the sources might well have taken place at considerably smaller velocities. Even so the ages fall in the range 10^5 to 10^6 years or 10^{13} seconds in order of magnitude and the cumulative emissions are as high as 2×10^{58} ergs.

Another method of determining the total energy involved in the radio sources is based on the assumption that the radio emission is synchrotron radiation from high energy electrons spiraling in a magnetic field extending throughout the object. This process is thought to be the most efficient for the generation of radio waves and accounts qualitatively at least for the linear polarization observed in many of the sources. The synchrotron theory implies that energy is *stored* in the radio objects in the form of magnetic field energy and relativistic electron energy. The magnetic field energy is proportional to the mean square of the field intensity (B) and to the volume. The total energy of the electrons is proportional to the rate at which they emit energy, the radio luminosity, divided by the three-halves power of the field intensity and the square root of the characteristic radio frequency emitted. Thus for a given observed volume, luminosity and radio emission spectrum the total energy is equal to a term proportional to B^2 plus one proportional to $B^{-3/2}$. One term increases as B increases while one term decreases. Thus the total energy exhibits a minimum as a function of B and this minimum can be readily determined. The values for the minimum stored energy exceed those of the minimum cumulative energies. In the case of the Hercules A source the minimum stored energy, if the high energy particles are electrons, is approximately 10^{60} ergs. The theory does not explicitly indicate the method by which the electrons are accelerated to high energy but it is reasonable to assume, as is the case in the cosmic radiation, that the nuclear component (mostly protons) of the neutral medium or plasma must have considerably greater total energy content than do the electrons. Upon taking this factor into account the stored energy in Hercules A, for example, is almost 10^{61} ergs. Because of their greater mass the protons do not take part in the synchrotron emission. On the other hand we can retain the lower value, 10^{60} ergs, if we assume that the neutral plasma consists of electrons and positrons and not protons.

In spite of the uncertainty in these minimum estimates it would seem that the stored energy which must be supplied in the initial galactic outburst is greater than the cumulative emission based on the minimum possible lifetimes. It may well be, as discussed above, that the velocities with which the linear dimensions of the sources increase are considerably less than that of light so that the characteristic age may be 10^7 or even 10^8 years and the stored energy is eventually released almost entirely at radio frequencies. Alternatively, as the radio emission region expands, the magnetic field may diminish to the point where the relativistic particles escape, carrying away a substantial fraction of the original energy. It has been suggested that, in this way, the radio galaxies may be the source of the cosmic radiation, and Geoffrey Burbidge has shown that the cosmic radiation could well permeate all of extragalactic space if this is the case.

In coming to a realistic estimate of the energy requirements in radio objects there remains the knotty problem concerning the efficiency with which the energy generated has been converted into relativistic particles and magnetic fields. Acceleration mechanisms employed in terrestrial laboratories are notoriously inefficient but this may well be due to the very small scale, astrophysically speaking, within which such mechanisms must operate. However, it is estimated that even in solar flares not more than a few per cent of the energy released is in the form of relativistic particles, the main energy release occurring in mass motions and electromagnetic radiation from x-rays to radio waves.

The most sanguine estimates must face the fact that all relativistic particles observed in nature, including cosmic rays and solar high energy particles, exhibit a spectrum of energies characterized by some inverse power law in energy, i.e., many more low energy particles are produced than high. The cut-off observed at the lowest energies may be due to the fact that low energy particles cannot escape from the region in which they are produced. The radio sources require electron energies in the one to 25 billion electron-volt range and it is difficult to believe that all the energy produced would be concentrated on these particles in this range. Synchrotron emission in the optical, x-ray, and gamma ray region must not be overlooked; neutrino emission cannot be ignored. Thus it can be argued that the radio emission efficiency is probably of the order of at most several per cent and the 10^{61} ergs quoted above should be increased considerably.

On the above basis, the figure 2×10^{62} ergs is frequently quoted as a representative value of the energy requirement in the larger radio sources and for the purposes of argument I will accept this as the *maximum* value in what follows. Suggestions have been made which modify the simple synchrotron model in such a way as to reduce the energy requirements. The magnetic field can be imagined to have a "clumpy" structure such that the effective emitting volume, where the field is highest, is much smaller than the overall volume observed. The magnetic field energy is proportional to the emitting volume, not the overall volume. The emission may come from groups of electrons radiating coherently and thus much more efficiently. Detailed studies of modifications along these lines will be necessary before the energy problem can be considered to be solved.

It will be noted that there is considerable disparity in the two estimates which it is possible to make for the energy *requirements* in the extended radio sources. On the one hand the *cumulative emissions* range up to 2×10^{58} ergs while the *stored energies* on the synchrotron model have been estimated to be as high as 2×10^{62} ergs.

SUPERMASSIVE STARS

The immensity of 2×10^{62} ergs can best be appreciated by a comparison with the equivalent rest mass energy of a single star, for example the sun. The mass of the sun is 2×10^{33} grams and the square of the velocity of light is $(3 \times 10^{10})^2 \sim 10^{21}$ ergs per gram. Thus Einstein's relation between energy and mass

$$E = Mc^2$$

becomes numerically

$$E \approx 2 \times 10^{54} \ (M/M_\odot) \text{ erg},$$

where $M/M_\odot$ is the stellar mass expected in units of the solar mass. We see then that the energy stored on the synchrotron theory in particles and magnetic fields in the invisible radio objects is of the order of that obtained by the complete annihilation of the mass of one hundred million suns, $10^8 \ M_\odot$. The problem can be taken in a literal sense on the grounds that the conversion of mass is the fundamental mechanism for the production of energy. On this basis the problem reduces to how, when, and where did the conversion take place.

Before proceeding, it is advisable to write Einstein's relation in a form more directly applicable to the problem under consideration as follows

$$\Delta E = (M_0 - M)c^2$$
$$= 2 \times 10^{54} \ (M_0 - M)/M_\odot \text{ erg},$$

where ΔE is the energy made available from a system of particles with total rest mass M_0 when by some mechanism the mass, measured through gravitational or inertial effects by an external observer, has been reduced to M. The quantity ΔE is the energy store available for transformation at varying efficiencies into the various observable forms—gamma ray, x-ray, optical, radio, neutrino, and high energy particle emission.

In principle it is possible for M to decrease to zero but not to negative values and so the maximum available energy is indeed $M_0 c^2$. One mechanism by which this can occur is through the annihilation of equal amounts of matter and antimatter. No detailed theory has been advanced showing how annihilation can take place in radio objects, the main problem having to do with the assembly of matter and antimatter in sufficient quantities on a time scale at most equal to that associated with the assumed explosive origin of these objects. Although annihilation will not be discussed further in this lecture, it may well prove to be the ultimate solution to the problem.

The success of the idea of nuclear energy generation in stars led quite naturally to the extension of this idea to the radio sources. In the summer of 1962 after conversations with Geoffrey and Margaret Burbidge at Cambridge University, Hoyle and I investigated the possibility that a very large mass in the range 10^3 to 10^{10} $M_\odot$ has condensed into a single *supermassive* star in which the energy generation takes place. On this point of view, using the standard theory of stellar structure in Newtonian hydrostatic equilibrium, one immediately obtains optical luminosities of the order of 10^{41} to 10^{48} erg sec^{-1} and lifetimes for nuclear energy generation of the order of 10^6 to 10^7 years so that the overall energy release can be as high as 10^{62} ergs.

There is, of course, a basic limitation inherent in thermonuclear energy generation. The conversion of hydrogen into helium involves the transformation of only 0.7 per cent of the rest mass into energy, and further nuclear burning leading to the most tightly bound nuclear species near iron brings this figure only to slightly less than one per cent. Thus $M_0 - M$ is at most equal to 0.01 M_0 and the complete nuclear conversion

of 10^8 solar masses of hydrogen into iron group elements leads
to the release of 2×10^{60} ergs. In general

$$\Delta E_{\text{nucl}} < 2 \times 10^{52} \, M_0/M_\odot \text{ erg.}$$

This equation is expressed in terms of an upper limit, for the
following reason. In the observed stars with masses ranging
approximately from 1 to 100 $M_\odot$ the conversion never seems
to reach completion before steady mass loss or supernova explosion terminates the life of the star. Thus it is clear that
the nuclear generation of 2×10^{62} ergs, the maximum value
discussed above, involves at least $10^{10} \, M_\odot$. This figure corresponds to the entire mass of a medium size galaxy! On the
other hand, the nuclear generation of 2×10^{58} ergs, the
minimum value discussed above, involves the order of $10^6 \, M_\odot$.
This figure corresponds to the mass of the larger globular
clusters of stars in the halo of our Galaxy and in other galaxies.
If globular clusters are involved in the energy production, it
need not necessarily take place at the center of the galaxy.

In the massive galaxies associated with the strong radio
sources there seemed to be no observational evidence for the
abnormal heavy element concentration which would presumably follow from the nuclear conversion of $10^{10} \, M_\odot$. If this
figure is to be accepted, Hoyle and I felt that nuclear energy is
probably inadequate and so we turned to another possibility,
gravitational energy. On classical Newtonian theory the gravitational binding energy of a system of rest mass M_0 with maximum radius R is approximately given by

$$\Omega \approx 2GM_0^2/R.$$

This expression includes a numerical coefficient (the 2) which
depends upon the distribution of matter in the star, but this
value is not crucial in the argument which follows. If no
energy is stored in the system, which remains as "cold" gas or
"dust," then Ω becomes ΔE_{grav}, the energy freed by the system
on condensing from the dispersed state in which the gravita-
tional interaction can be neglected. Thus

$$\Delta E_{\text{grav}} = \Omega \approx (2GM_0/Rc^2) \, M_0 c^2.$$

It will be seen that the dimensionless quantity $2GM_0/Rc^2$ is just the fraction of the rest mass energy made available. Classical Newtonian theory places no limitation on $2GM_0/Rc^2$ but the theory of general relativity limits it to the order of unity in the approximation here under consideration. Thus

$$\Delta E_{\mathrm{grav}} \leqq M_0 c^2$$
$$\leqq 2 \times 10^{54} \, M_0/M_\odot \, \mathrm{erg}$$

in agreement with the statement made previously that M could not become negative.

In what way can use be made of the release of gravitational energy? We assume that in some way this energy is transferred from the collapsing core of a massive star to the outer envelope which is thus blown off with high velocity and high internal energy. The transfer may be ordinary radiative heat transfer by photons or it might be accomplished by neutrino emission from the core with absorption in the envelope. Curtis Michel made an ingenious suggestion which does not require the emitted neutrinos to be reabsorbed. (Neutrino absorption cross sections are very small.) He suggested that the effective gravitational mass of the core might be reduced considerably by the loss of the neutrino energy, thus reducing the gravitational attraction on the envelope to the point where the internal thermal energy of the outer material is then sufficient to explode it away from the core with high velocity. Another possibility exists if the massive star is in rotation. After the exhaustion of nuclear energy the star will contract, the contraction of the core being much more rapid than that of the envelope. It is reasonable to suppose that the angular momentum of the core will be conserved once it has contracted away from the envelope and that eventually the core will become unstable to fission into two bodies rotating about each other as in a binary star. Such a system loses rotational energy by radiating gravitational waves (or gravitons in particle parlance) and thus again the effective mass of the core system is reduced as in Michel's model.

All such models suffer from the limiting effect of the *gravita-*

tional red shift. In order for gravitational energy to be released from the core it is necessary that the core contract or that $(2GM/Rc^2)_{core}$ increase. But the gravitational red shift in radiation is just proportional to this dimensionless quantity in first order. In fact it is approximately equal to one-half this quantity or to $(GM/Rc^2)_{core}$. Radiation arrives at a distant observer with less energy than that calculated by a local observer where the radiation is emitted. This is true for all forms of energy transfer, by particles as well as radiation. Thus the rate of any form of energy loss by the core is greatly reduced as $(GM/Rc^2)_{core}$ increases and, as a result, the energy loss is not *complete* as implied in the preceding discussion where it was assumed that no internal energy of motion or radiation remained in the star during contraction. As a matter of fact even the most optimistic calculations have not revealed mechanisms whereby a contracting massive star can transfer more than a few per cent of the gravitational energy of its core to the outer envelope. The gravitational release of energy may be somewhat more efficient than nuclear release but not by a large factor. Thus the release of 2×10^{62} ergs must, on just about any grounds, involves a mass of the order of $10^{10} M_\odot$. If this figure is indeed the correct value for the energy requirement in radio galaxies, then at least one per cent of the mass of the galaxy has been involved in the generation of this energy. The mass of the large elliptical galaxies is estimated to be $10^{12} M_\odot$.

DISCOVERY OF THE QUASARS

It has been noted previously that Hoyle and I had obtained *optical* luminosities up to 10^{48} erg sec^{-1} for a supermassive star in hydrostatic equilibrium and in fact we found that the luminosity is just proportional to the mass for $M > 10^3 M_\odot$. These large optical luminosities did not seem to have any immediate connection with the extended radio sources since the problem concerning the transformation of the optically emitted energy into high energy electrons and magnetic fields remained unsolved.

However, at the same time that our calculations were being

made in Cambridge an observational discovery of great signifi
cance was made in Pasadena by Maarten Schmidt and was
quickly confirmed by J. B. Oke and by Jesse L. Greenstein and
Thomas A. Matthews. It had been known for some time that
certain of the radio sources were located in coincidence with
starlike objects which apparently had diameters too small to be
resolved by optical telescopes and which showed on photographic plates as diffraction images characteristic of the telescope. These objects were called *radio stars*.

The Pasadena group pioneered in the use of the 200-inch
Hale telescope on Mount Palomar to investigate the spectroscopy of these radio stars. For several years their investigations of four of these objects led nowhere; they were unable to
understand the peculiar emission lines of the spectra which the
telescope revealed. There the matter rested until Schmidt
began studying the spectrum of a fifth object catalogued by
Cambridge University radio astronomers as 3C 273. Using
occultation by the moon, a group of radio astronomers in
Australia led by Cyril Hazard had shown that the detailed
structure of the radio emission by 3C 273 indicated that radio
stars were certainly not stars in the ordinary sense but were a
new class of astronomical object.

This time the Gordian knot was cut. Several of the emission
lines from 3C 273 formed a simple harmonic pattern, with
separation and intensity decreasing toward the ultraviolet.
The lines obviously belonged to a series of the type expected
from hydrogen or any other atom that had been stripped of
all electrons but one. Schmidt soon concluded that no atom
gave the observed wave lengths. If he assumed, however, that
the spectrum lines had been shifted toward the red by 16
per cent, the observed wave lengths agreed with those of
hydrogen. Shortly thereafter Oke found the Hα-line in exactly
the position predicted by the red-shift hypothesis and Greenstein and Matthews found an even greater red shift of 37 per
cent in 3C 48 when they properly identified the lines observed
as corresponding to well-known lines from the elements oxygen,
neon, and magnesium. In the interval since these early dis-

coveries, optical observations on additional radio stars have revealed cases for which the observed wave lengths are as much as three times the laboratory wave lengths.

Greenstein and Schmidt soon showed that the red shifts could not be gravitational red shifts associated with large masses confined to regions of very small radius.[2] The masses involved are found to be quite large but the radii of the emitting regions are so great that the gravitational red shift is negligible. They suggested that the *quasi-stellar* objects or *quasars* are extragalactic and that the red shifts arise from the general cosmological expansion of the universe. With this interpretation they were then able to determine the luminosity distance for the objects and to convert the observed apparent luminosities into absolute luminosities. The calculations indicated that the quasars have optical luminosities of the order of 10^{46} erg sec^{-1} or more than one thousand times the optical luminosity of our Galaxy. The quasars may or may not be located in galaxies, but if they are, they outshine the surrounding galaxy so that it is lost in the diffraction pattern of the quasar image.

The Great Quasar Controversy

Recently the quasars have become the subject of lively controversy. The final answers are just not known at the present time but permit me to continue with a few relevant observations.

It is now well established that the quasars exhibit variability in radio and optical luminosity. In addition to luminous flashes with durations of the order of days or weeks, there is some evidence for cyclic variations in the optical luminosity with periods of the order of ten years. It is generally agreed that

---

[2] As these pages go to print early in 1967, Fred Hoyle and I have suggested a model for the quasars for which the red shift may be gravitational. In this model the light originates in a supermassive cloud of luminous gas located at the center of a large number of clusters of stars or other sub-units. The stellar clusters produce the gravitational potential which red shifts the emission and absorption lines from the cloud. Lines in the stellar spectra are smeared out by the rapid motions of the stars. The arguments of Greenstein and Schmidt do not apply to this model.

the occurrence of the cyclic variations is crucial to the question whether the primary radiation object is a single coherent massive star $(10^3 - 10^{10}\ M_\odot)$ as originally proposed by Hoyle and me or a system of smaller stars $(1-10^2\ M_\odot)$ as discussed by numerous authors, Geoffrey Burbidge, Thomas Gold, Lodewyk Woltjer, Stanley Ulam, and George Field. It is difficult, on the basis of collisions or supernova outbursts in a system of many stellar objects, to explain variations which exhibit a fairly regular periodicity. However, a regular periodicity with periods of the order of several years is characteristic of the pulsations of massive objects. Only additional and more precise observations will settle this matter.

It has also been suggested that the quasars are *local*. James Terrell has proposed the hypothesis that the quasars were ejected at relativistic velocities in an explosive event at the center of the Galaxy about five million years ago. Hoyle and Burbidge have suggested that a likely candidate to give rise to the quasars in our vicinity is NGC 5128, the powerful radio source previously discussed in which at least two outbursts appear to have occurred. In this case some objects with blue shifts may be expected. Halton Arp claims to have observed that several greatly red-shifted quasars are associated with nearby *peculiar* galaxies which have small red shifts. Arp concludes that the quasars are local and that their red shift is not due to the universal Hubble expansion.

On the *local* hypothesis the characteristic distances for the quasars are 1 to 10 megaparsecs rather than 10^3 to 10^4 megaparsecs as on the *cosmological* hypothesis. The megaparsec is a distance equal to three million light years or 3×10^{24} centimeters. Terrell suggests that the quasar masses are approximately $10^4\ M_\odot$ rather than the value 10^8 to $10^{10}\ M_\odot$ required if the observed red shifts are cosmological. *Thus on either the local or the cosmological hypothesis, supermassive stars, as defined in this lecture, are required.* Furthermore, the original local outburst involved masses of the same order of magnitude as those attributed to the quasars themselves on the cosmological hypothesis. Consequently, in the remainder of the lecture reference to the quasars will be made on the basis that they are cosmological objects but this is not a necessary condition for the arguments put forward.

ENERGY RESOURCES

The optical luminosities of the quasars are very high, $\sim 10^{46}$ erg sec^{-1}, but there is no convincing evidence that these objects have lifetimes in excess of 10^5 to 10^6 years. Thus the cumulative optical emission is the order of 10^{59} ergs, which is well within the nuclear resources of a star with $M = 10^8\ M_\odot$. Only seven per cent of the hydrogen of such a massive star need be converted into helium to release this amount of energy.

These considerations lead to the final question: Are the cores of supermassive stars stable or unstable during nuclear burning? For spherically symmetric, nonrotating configurations the answer is "No" for the cases with $M > 10^6\ M_\odot$.

Richard Feynman has pointed out in lectures to his class in relativity that general relativistic instabilities set in very early in the evolution of a spherically symmetric supermassive star. Icko Iben, Jr., proved the existence of these instabilities in detailed numerical calculations. James Wright and I have been independently able to show that, even in the post-Newtonian approximation to hydrostatic equilibrium, general relativistic effects lead to dynamic instability for supermassive stars. Subrahmanyan Chandrasekhar has given a very elegant proof of this instability using the full panoply of the exact equations of general relativity. For supermassive stars with $M \sim 10^3$ to $10^6\ M_\odot$ the instability sets in at approximately the stage of contraction where hydrogen burning can also take place at the center of the star. It is possible to show that relaxation oscillations are triggered by the sudden onset of nuclear burning during contraction arising from the instability. These oscillations are damped by the very great luminosity of the quasi-stellar object. The calculated periods are the order of ten years, in agreement with the observations of Harlan Smith and Dorrit Hoffleit on the variability of 3C 273. Shock waves transmit the nuclear energy to the tenuous outer regions of the quasar, where optical line emission and radio emission are

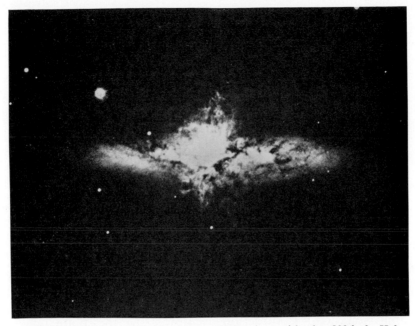

Fig. 24. Photograph of the galaxy M82 taken with the 200-inch Hale telescope on Mount Palomar in Hα light. Note the complex filamentary structure expanding from the center of the galaxy. Roger Lynds and Allen Sandage point out that the total mass of the expanding material could be as great as 5.6×10^6 $M_\odot$. This exceeds the mass which can be stabilized during hydrogen burning by ordinary pressure forces because of general relativistic effects. It is suggested that the explosion is the result of the general relativistic instability discussed in the text. (*Mount Wilson and Palomar Observatories.*)

stimulated. The radio emission originates in the outermost regions, where the shock wave becomes relativistic and electrons are accelerated to relativistic energies.

For masses greater than 10^6 $M_\odot$, nuclear burning does not lead to stable oscillations but takes place explosively. This could well account for the explosion (fig. 24) observed in the galaxy M82 in which Roger Lynds and Allen Sandage point out that the total mass of the expanding material could be as great as 5.6×10^6 $M_\odot$. There are many other galaxies which show evidence of explosive events. I recall with great delight a sentence which appeared in *Time* Magazine:

Astrophysicists Fred Hoyle and William A. Fowler, from

Caltech, told the American Physical Society that galaxies *often* explode with *improbable* energy.

The *italics* are mine!

It is important to emphasize that the general relativistic instability follows from the assumption of spherical symmetry. The instability reflects the fact that pressure support from gas and radiation alone is insufficient to guarantee *stable* hydrostatic equilibrium in a spherically symmetric supermassive star. It is thus necessary to give up the special symmetry inherent in spherical collapse and to look to other mechanisms which will lead to stability, dynamic or static, in supermassive stars for lifetimes comparable to the estimates made for the quasi-stellar objects. One possibility is rotation. A large initial rotation can lead to a flattened disk configuration which can fragment into smaller stars with characteristic times of stable evolution comparable to those required. Even relatively small rotations remove the general relativistic instability in the post-Newtonian approximation. Contraction is slowed to the point where hydrogen burning can be effective in triggering and maintaining oscillations in stars with masses considerably in excess of the 10^6 $M_\odot$ limit found for the nonrotating case, perhaps so great as 10^9 $M_\odot$.

The wide range in masses possible for the quasars leads to a consequence of great significance. Since the absolute luminosity is proportional to the mass, quasars will also exhibit a wide range in absolute magnitude. Thus the red shift—apparent magnitude plots for quasars should not consist of a single line but of a broad band with width characteristic of the spread in absolute luminosity. The observations to date seem to bear this out.

It would take us too far afield to discuss stability and rotation in more detail in this lecture. It can be concluded that the nuclear and gravitational resources of sufficiently massive condensations are indeed able to meet reasonable estimates for the energy requirements in the strong radio sources and quasi-stellar objects. Nuclear energy is made available during the stable epoch of stellar evolution, during which rotation and

general relativity play dominant roles in contrast to the situa
tion in less massive stars. Gravitational energy, somewhat
greater in magnitude than nuclear energy, becomes available in
the ultimate stage of stellar evolution when the nuclear resources are exhausted and instability leads to gravitational
collapse. The quasars shine on nuclear energy. Gravitational
energy release leads to the development of the extended radio
sources. These conclusions are subject to the usual proviso
associated with developments in a rapidly developing field of
observation and theoretical study. We are almost certainly in
for a number of surprises before we understand the extended
radio sources and the quasars. These celestial objects have not
revealed all of their secrets by any means!